The Ideas of Biology

THE IDEAS OF BIOLOGY

by

JOHN TYLER BONNER

drawings by

Anne L. Cox

Harper Modern Science Series
edited by James R. Newman

HARPER TORCHBOOKS
The Science Library
HARPER & ROW, PUBLISHERS
NEW YORK

To My Mother

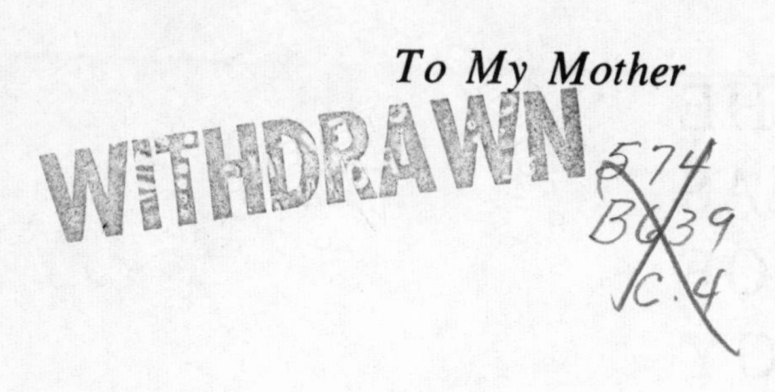

THE IDEAS OF BIOLOGY

Printed in the United States of America

This book was originally published in 1962 by Harper & Brothers in the Harper Modern Science Series, edited by James R. Newman.

First HARPER TORCHBOOK edition published 1964 by
Harper & Row, Publishers, Incorporated
New York and Evanston

Library of Congress catalog card number: 62-9884

CONTENTS

ACKNOWLEDGMENTS

I am very grateful to the following individuals for their help in reading some or all of the manuscript: B. M. Eberhart, L. I. Rebhun, and W. F. Zimmerman.

I should like to thank Drs. W. Beerman, Th. Dobzhansky and N. Tinbergen for permission to use their illustrations.

I should also like to express my gratitude to the following publishers for permission to use illustrations: Oxford University Press, Fig. 21; The Scientific American, Fig. 24; John Wiley & Sons, Inc., Figs. 11, 12.

PREFACE

Perhaps more than any other science, biology is a staggeringly large collection of facts. This poses a great problem in an elementary course of biology because the mere accumulation of these facts is a large task and leaves little time to see what they mean and how they fit together. It is not unheard of for students to fail utterly to see the point, the meaning of this refuse heap of information until the end of the course; or it may hit them in a flash during the final examination; or worse, they may never see it, and the unhinged facts may soon wash away from their minds.

The main purpose of textbooks is to present the facts in as simple and orderly a fashion as possible so that the student can learn them and keep them straight. The main purpose of this book is to assume this basic information and then to stand off as far as possible and see what it means. This is a book on the ideas rather than the facts of biology, although, of course, the ideas have the facts as their foundations. We want the facts, because with them we can see the ideas; but if there is just time for the facts it is like eating a cake without the icing. This book is not a textbook; it is all icing.

In other words the material given here is intended to go along with the biology text. It is written as supplementary reading, perhaps to be undertaken in the latter part of a first-year biology course. However, it is not so dependent upon a text that it cannot be read by the intelligent layman who wishes to discover some of the larger themes of biology today.

Turning now to the themes themselves, all biologists I think would agree that evolution is the largest and most encompassing of them all. Evolution has provided the framework for life in general, and therefore it will be the frame of this book. But before discussing this central theme it may be helpful to examine the lesser one of the living machine itself. Of course this machine, which is basically the cell, has come into being as a step in evolution; but it will be easier to understand the origin of life and later evolutionary developments if we first know something of the workings of the living system.

As soon as the mechanics of evolution are clear then we shall see that the prime element is a controlled method of producing stable variations in offspring. This is the study of heredity or genetics, and it will be possible to show that genetics and evolution operate hand in glove in the course of biological progress.

One of the consequences of increased size and complexity of animals and plants during the course of evolution is that there is an embryonic development, a steady unfolding of the fertilized egg to produce the intricate, functioning adult. On the one hand we can see the relation of development to genetics and evolution, and on the other we can examine what we know and understand of the process of development itself. This inquiry will also emphasize what we do not know, for biology is a science in which there remain many important unsolved problems.

Another consequence of the increase in size and complexity of organisms during evolution is that over and above elaborate systems of communication and control between cells, as in developing organisms, this communication can also be extended beyond the organism to produce colonial organisms and even social organisms, such as the social insects, the ants, and the bees. Furthermore, there may be associations between members of different species, sometimes where one gains and the other loses, as in parasitism, and others in which both species appear to gain as in symbiosis. Lastly organisms are in constant communication with their whole environment; this results in the balance of nature where the activities of the entire community of animals and plants interlock and are interdependent. In fact it is in this ecological setting that we catch the evolutionary mechanism in operation.

The whole of life is in a sense a unit, for changes in any part affect all other parts.

Finally it is of interest to apply some of these ideas of biology to man and to consider his development, his genetics, and his evolution. It is even possible and, moreover, important to consider his ecology, his changing role on the face of the earth, and the consequences to his environment, to the other animals and plants that surround him, and to his own future.

CHAPTER 1

THE CELL

We think of a cell as being a small unit that makes up a plant or an animal. "Small" is a rather vague way of putting it, and it would be more precise to say that a cell has a diameter of roughly 8 to 15 microns (a micron is 1/1000th of a millimeter). Perhaps it would be more helpful to put it still another way. A cell is so small that a human being is made up of over a million-million (10^{12}) of them. This means that if a man is enlarged to the size of an average living room then a cell in his body would roughly be the size of a pinhead.

One of the astounding facts of life is that the cells of all animals and plants (with the exception of bacteria) from the smallest amoeba to the largest elephant and from the minute algae in the sea to the giant redwood are all roughly the same in construction. They all have a roundish nucleus surrounded by cytoplasm. Within the nucleus they all possess chromosomes that bear the genes, the factors of inheritance; and within the cytoplasm they all have similar particles, such as mitochondria. For the most part their cytoplasm is bordered by a thin cell membrane, although there are certain interesting organisms or parts of organisms that lack this membrane and have nuclei all wandering about in one large mass of cytoplasm. This is true, for instance, in early stages of development of a number of plants and animals. But these exceptions, as will be shown presently, have little meaning when one considers the cell not as a unit of structure but as a unit of function.

If the structure of all cells is basically similar, it is not surprising to find that their function or functions are similar as well. Their most important function is that of energy turnover; they take in fuel and convert the energy from the fuel into all the living activities, for example, cell movement. Each cell is a minute motor, or, to phrase it in a more conventional manner, each cell is a unit of metabolism. Another function, that they perform with the energy derived from the metabolism is to reproduce, to duplicate parts. This is the basis of growth and reproduction in which the living substance can, in essence, make more of itself. A third function is one of responsiveness, or irritability, as it is sometimes called. This means that a cell can respond to stimuli, and in this way it can react to its environment and to other cells that may surround it. It is a combination of awareness and co-ordination that is really a characteristic of any motor, any energy machine; the wheels of a car respond to a push on the steering wheel, and the engine puffs in response to a steep hill.

Now that the outline of what can be said about a cell is spread before us, let us examine the matter in more detail. What we want to know is how this motor works, how it is put together, and what makes it run.

Although a cell is a motor, it clearly does not have wheels and gears inside like a wrist watch. Instead it can more properly be described as a chemical machine in somewhat the way a battery is a chemical machine (although the differences are great). Therefore, presumably, if one knew something of the chemical constituents of a cell, one might learn something important about its operation.

At first this seems to be a rather discouraging approach, because with a few quick calculations one can soon see that even though a cell is small it contains a very large number of chemical molecules, for molecules are themselves so small. In fact an average size cell contains about 200 million-million (2×10^{14}) molecules. This means that if one enlarged the pinhead that was the cell to the size of a reasonably large room, then each molecule within the cell would be about the size of a pinpoint. This staggering thought so severely taxes the imagination that any idea of seeing how this bag full of millions of molecules can work seems out of the question; there are too many parts to the machine to ever make any sense of it.

Furthermore, it is not very helpful to analyze the problem at a lower level. Molecules, from the smallest, such as hydrogen, to the largest proteins are made up of protons, electrons, and neutrons. These particles, with all the others inside the atomic nucleus, are ubiquitous. This means that living organisms are not alone in being made up of electrons, protons, and neutrons; this is true of all matter. A table, a glass of water, a layer of dust, or the slate of a tombstone are nothing more than masses of these three basic particles. This answers nothing and only emphasizes what we seek: what is special about the substance of living cells; how does it differ from that of the nonliving world?

The answer lies partly in the fact that the atoms and molecules in a cell are special and their combinations specific. For instance, of the hundred odd kinds of atoms or elements present on earth only a limited number are present in living substance. In fact there are only four—oxygen, carbon, hydrogen, and nitrogen—that are present in any abundance at all. The various components of salts—calcium, phosphorus, potassium, sodium, chlorine, and magnesium—are present in very small amounts. The remaining substances worth mentioning are exceedingly scarce: iron, manganese, copper, zinc, sulfur, iodine, silicon, and fluorine.

These atoms combine to form many thousands of compounds or molecules characteristic of cells. Besides water there are the different carbohydrates, fats, and proteins; these are the most abundant groups of substances. Furthermore, there are the nucleic acids, salts, and a host of substances, such as the vitamins, that are present in small quantities.

A little order to this gigantic problem within a minute cell is emerging. We must now lean upon the biochemist, who has been so successful in the last few decades, and ask what these groups of substances do and how they operate as part of the cell machinery. Many of the detailed answers are still a matter of active research, but the broad answers that we seek here are known.

To begin with, a number of substances supply fuel; that is they are burned or broken down to release energy, just as a motorcar burns gasoline. The most obvious examples are carbohydrates, which consist, among other things, of simple, energy-rich sugars. Another related use of carbohydrates is the storage of fuel. The sugar molecules can be hooked together and put out of circulation, out of immediate use, in the form of starch. If they are needed for energy during a period of starvation, they can easily be broken apart, and the sugar molecules can again be available. Very much the same situation is found in fats. The component parts of fats, the fatty acids, are fuel, and the larger fat molecules are again convenient as food storage. Even proteins show this pattern, and amino acids can also be conserved as an energy source.

Some substances are specifically associated with support; that is they provide the hard skeletal material necessary to give an animal or a plant backbone. Cellulose, for instance, is a rigid carbohydrate that is responsible for the fact that delicate flowers can rise into the air and giant trees tower over our heads. (It is even present in some animals, namely the ascidians or sea squirts.) The related compound chitin is found in some lower plants, but its prime importance is in the hard exo- or outside skeleton of insects and other arthropods. Some supporting substances are composed of proteins. A striking example is the tough collagen that makes tendons and similar tissues in animals; another is hair and its relatives—the feathers of birds; the horns of rhinoceroses or sheep; the scales of fish, snakes, and lizards; the nails of one's fingers; or the claws of a cat. Finally, calcium salts are often used either alone or in conjunction with an organic matrix to form the hard bone of mammals, the exoskeleton of a lobster, the stalk of a coral, or the antler of a deer.

Besides food, food storage, and skeletal support, there is quite another cell function associated with specific chemical constituents. This is heredity where the information concerning cell structure is passed from one generation to the next. This information is somehow coded in the chromosomes within the nucleus, and there is now overwhelming evidence that nucleic acids are associated with this holding and transfer of information. One of the reasons these substances appear to be so suited for this function is that they are chemically very stable, and they can retain the information and pass it on with relatively few errors or changes.

From the point of view of cell machinery perhaps the most important substances are the enzymes. These all consist of large protein molecules, and within a minute cell there are vast numbers of different kinds of enzymes. Their function is highly specific; each particular enzyme controls or polices a particular chemical reaction. For instance, if starch is to be split into its component sugar molecules, this reaction can be guided by a protein enzyme whose only job is to mediate this breakdown of starch.

The nature of enzymes brings us very close to the subject of energy, and this will be the opportune moment to pause in our discussion of cell constituents and see how the cell can operate as an energy machine. It will be a switch from cell chemistry to cell physics.

Let us begin with a dash of some very elementary physics, because one thing that seems fairly certain is that living organisms do not defy any physical principles. The laws of physics are as meaningful for an animal as they are for any inert object.

The cell is small, and within there are many molecules floating about although others may be bound to membranes and other cell structures. According to the kinetic theory of gases, unless the cell is at absolute zero (−273° C.) all these molecules will be in constant motion. Cells would be in a kind of suspended animation at that low temperature; in fact protoplasm is usually unhappy below freezing (0° C.) because of the formation of ice crystals. In arctic plants cells cease all activity in the winter, and the higher animals are warm blooded to keep them going. Therefore, when cells are active there is a considerable amount of molecular movement within.

Even the largest molecules are too small to be seen in a light microscope, but a molecule in motion can bump against a minute visible particle and move it. This is a very general phenomenon that can be demonstrated in suspensions of all sorts, but it was first discovered in the living pollen cell of a plant by the botanist Robert Brown in the nineteenth century. The complete understanding of the physics of the phenomenon of "Brownian movement," as it is called, was not understood until the work of Einstein in this century. The fact that it is a phenomenon not necessarily associated with life was forceably demonstrated to me a few years ago. I was examining some dusty old microscope slides prepared in the 1890's that formed part of a collection in a botanical museum. While looking at the cells with the high powers of a microscope, I received a severe shock, for there was movement inside some of the cells that had remained imprisoned in balsam glue for more than fifty years. When reason returned I knew that I was not observing life-movements but Brownian movement. There was still liquid inside the cells and enough barely visible particles to be pushed about by the molecular motion.

Although this movement of molecules is a simple physical phenomenon found in dead cells and suspensions, living cells also make use of it. By means of this movement diffusion takes place, and diffusion is all important to cells as a means of transporting substances from one place to another. If there is a high concentration of a substance at a particular spot, this eventually dissipates and spreads so that the substance is evenly distributed everywhere. For instance, if one places a drop of dye in a still glass of water, for a period one region only will be colored, but later the whole glass will have uniformly tinted water. This is because the dye molecules move; they bump into one another and bounce about until finally when equilibrium is reached they are spread over a large area. It is even possible, if there is a membrane that prevents a molecule (such as sugar) from moving while the solvent (water) can pass easily through the small holes of the membrane, to prevent or confine the sugar diffusion. But the water keeps pushing in through the membrane by diffusion to dilute the sugar, and the result is that the bag containing the sugar becomes very turgid; it has a positive internal pressure, which is called osmotic pressure. This is precisely what happens to cells; diffusion and its molecular motion is a manifestation of energy that affects living systems.

One final thing should be said here about molecular motion. As was already implied the degree of motion corresponds directly with the temperature, and this fact is referred to under the rather general name of kinetic theory of gases. While all motion ceases at absolute zero, it increases as the temperature rises. This increase is not exactly smooth but has some interesting discontinuities. These discontinuities or states are solid, liquid, and gas. If water is below 0° C. then it is ice; above 0° C. it is water; and above 100° C. it is water vapor or steam. The difference in these states can be entirely attributed to the difference in the activity of the molecules at different temperatures. This means, furthermore, that heat is no more than molecular motion, and the hotter a substance the more intensely its component molecules move.

We are in this short skirmish with physics really interested in energy, and we have shown that energy can manifest itself in terms of molecular motion. This is, of course, not the only kind of energy. For instance, there is chemical energy, the energy given off by a chemical reaction. There is mechanical energy, the simple pushing and pulling of the pistons of an engine or of our arms and legs. There is electrical energy, which is so useful in our modern living. Finally there is radiation energy. The energy that is given off in the form of light or heat waves from shining light bulbs, hot irons, or the blazing sun.

There is an old and somewhat disconcerting principle called the law of conservation of energy. This means that energy can neither be created nor destroyed and that machines of perpetual motion are impossible. What child has not spent hours trying to devise a machine that keeps going with rolling balls and magnets; it is one of the pains of growing up to find that it cannot be so. Every time one has seemingly created or destroyed the energy, in reality it has only been converted from one form to another. There is the old problem of taking a steel spring, coiling it very tight so that it is full of potential mechanical energy, and placing it in an acid bath. When the steel is gone has the energy not been destroyed? The answer is no, for the heat of the acid bath is higher because the spring has been coiled; the energy has slyly become converted to heat.

More obvious examples of conversion are easy to find. Chemical energy is converted to heat in wood fire; chemical energy is converted to mechanical energy in the piston of a car; mechanical energy is converted to electrical energy in an electrical generator; radiant energy is converted to chemical energy on a photographic plate. The examples could be greatly extended, but they are so obvious that there is no need.

Most energy changes seem to occur in one great rush, and then once equilibrium is reached there is a complete stop. This is not true, however, of a gasoline motor. As long as fuel is added and as long as the mechanical parts do not collapse, the chemical energy is continuously converted into mechanical energy along with some loss of energy into heat that dissipates into the air. This condition where energy continually pours in and is continuously converted is called a *steady state*. It is a sort of unending equilibrium. In this living organisms exactly parallel engines in operation, for they continually take in fuel, and they continually convert it to mechanical energy, other types of chemical energy, and heat. In the case of animals the fuels are primarily fats, carbohydrates, and proteins. Green plants, on the other hand, convert radiant energy. The sun's rays hit the molecules of chlorophyll that as a result become highly active and frenzied in their motion. In this way they are capable of encouraging carbon dioxide and water to combine to form sugars. Then their cells proceed to use the sugars or chemical fuel in the same way as do animal cells. Green plants simply have an extra conversion step, but in both cases while alive they remain in a steady state. Complete and final equilibrium comes only in death.

Clearly there are great differences between a gasoline engine and a cell despite their similarity as energy converters. Already we have shown that while one has gears and pistons the other is no more than a bag of a great heterogeneous mass of chemicals. Another difference is that engines are made of substances very different from their fuel—otherwise the engine would consume itself in one burst —but organisms are constructed of the same substances as their fuel, and cannibals live happily on their fellow men.

At first it would seem impossible to burn combustible materials in a furnace that is itself combustible. But the way living cells do this is a vital key to their nature. They have found a method of burning the food very slowly, so slowly that there is no flash of all-consuming heat but only a slight glow that keeps the body warm. In essence it is controlled combustion, and the control is exerted in two ways. In the first place the burning process is divided into a series of lesser energy-releasing chemical reactions, and secondly each of these is controlled as far as its rate of reaction is concerned by an enzyme. It is like taking many small steps instead of one bone-shattering leap. When earlier we said that enzymes control reactions, we meant particularly that they control their rate or that, in other words, enzymes are catalysts. They are the policemen who keep a firm grip on all chemical changes; they see to it that no reaction breaks any speed laws.

I do not know how many chemical reactions occur within a cell, but there must be a very large number; and if each of the reactions is controlled by a particular, specific enzyme—add to this the reacting substances and their products—then the final picture is one of a chemical engine with an incredible number of different kinds of parts despite its small size. Admittedly there are 200 million-million molecules: this gives plenty of leeway for a complex machine, but the final picture is still very unsatisfactory as far as any clear view of the cell engine is concerned.

The proper thing to do at this juncture, although it is an impossibly large topic for the scope of this book, would be to describe all that is known in modern biochemistry of these chemical reactions and the energy pathways. This is a field of intensive and active research at the moment, and while many of the steps are known, far more are still obscure and waiting to be understood by the experimenter. There is a wealth of information on the processing or metabolism of carbohydrates, and perhaps this is one of the best understood series of chemical reactions. It is instructive in many ways, but most especially it shows that each reaction is a reversible one and that the burning of sugar from which energy is released is the opposite from the synthesis of sugar for which energy is required. Obviously a cell must be able to do both, for otherwise it could never grow. Therefore, one of the ways energy derived from food is used is to provide energy for the uphill synthetic reactions that need a special push. This very same principle was already illustrated in the case of photosynthesis of green plant cells where the radiant energy of the sun activates a chlorophyll molecule, and this energized molecule can reverse a reaction that would normally go downhill and release energy; it pushes the reaction uphill by giving it energy, and the result is the synthesis of sugar.

Besides the synthesis of new substances that is so essential for maintenance and growth, there is also a rather special kind of synthesis that is important to cells that might be called the replication of molecules. Again this is a field of intensive research, for its importance is universally recognized. One of the ways large protein enzymes, for instance, can be so specific lies in the small details of their structure. Proteins are made up of amino acids strung together and there are some twenty-four such building blocks. They can be put together in a great variety of different combinations, and a particular combination presumably gives rise to a particular specific protein. The same situation holds true for the nucleic acids, which are made up of a series of four different kinds of building blocks that are hooked together on a very long backbone of sugars in a chain. Presumably again the specificity of these substances is related to the way in which the four side chains are hooked together. It is thought that their configuration provides some kind of a code. In the nucleic acids of the chromosome this is presumed to be the basis of hereditary traits of the individual.

These substances are so complex that they could not be synthesized without some cue, some helping guide, so that a substance of a particular configuration can be produced at will. In the case of nucleic acids there is considerable evidence that one chain manufactures a daughter chain alongside it by bringing the constituent groups of atoms next to it in the proper places to form a new, identical daughter molecule. This kind of synthesis is sometimes called template synthesis because the parent molecule acts as a mold, a template. In the case of proteins the evidence strongly suggests that particular kinds of nucleic acids (ribonucleic acid or RNA) manufacture complex proteins in the same way. They serve as molds for the large and specific protein molecules. The nucleic acids on the chromosomes (presumably the genes) are of a slightly different chemical nature, and they are called desoxyribonucleic acids or DNA. They can duplicate themselves in the manner described when the cell divides, and they can also effect by synthesis the configuration of the RNA and, therefore, the specific proteins. In our analogy to the cell as a small motor this type of synthesis by replication is a system where the motor can keep renewing its used and worn parts, and it can even make new motors the very mirror of itself. We begin to see that the cell is an engine of no small abilities; in fact for a miniscule bag of chemicals its efficiency of operation is utterly astounding.

One final word concerning cell activities and cell energetics: The point has been made that the energy derived from food (or from the sun's radiation in the case of green plants) is partly converted and dissipated in the form of heat and partly used as a source of energy in the various types of synthesis of new chemical constituents. There is a further important use of this energy, and that is it provides the means whereby the cell can move, often in response to its environment. For instance, many cells may show some sort of contraction if they are jolted in any way. Of course, the muscle cells of higher animals are particularly adept at movement, but all cells are capable of it to some degree. In some cases the whole cell will wander, as with amoebae; in others the cell may be confined within a hard cell wall, as in the case for many plant cells, and the cytoplasm will stream about within its prison. The mechanism of movement is hardly understood at all (despite many attacks on the problem) with the notable exception of the functioning of animal muscle where great progress has been made in recent years. Apparently there are special contractile protein molecules that lie in a well-knit, organized structure, and with the proper stimulus, a chemical reaction occurs that results in the contraction. Many details of the process are still wanting, but the main outlines are known.

The fact that cells respond in this and other ways to stimuli is recognized by the term irritability, and these responses in general require energy. Again it is difficult to analyze the responses in isolated single cells, but if one looks to the complex receptors of animals, the mechanism is boldly emphasized and can readily be approached by experiment. For instance, in the case of the eye certain cells contain a pigment that is light sensitive, much as is the emulsion of a photographic film. When the light hits this pigment it changes its chemical structure and results in an energy change that sets up a nerve impulse that is carried to the brain. Essentially the same happens with the ear; sound waves stimulate the sensitive cells in the ear, and they in turn respond to the energy change by initiating a nerve impulse that informs the brain. This is true as well for the smell, touch, and taste receptors. In each case a cell or group of cells is especially sensitive to an external energy change of a particular sort, and this is converted by the responding cell to a nerve impulse.

Moreover, these impulses and their conduction use energy that has been provided through the fuel, the food. Admittedly the amount of energy required is small, and thinking, despite one's personal feelings on the subject, requires far less energy in terms of food than chopping wood. There is a wave that follows along the membrane of the nerve in which salts are suddenly allowed to pass freely through the membrane, in this way continually propagating the impulse. It is like a burning fuse in that the energy for its process is provided all along the road as it moves. Then once the impulse has passed the used nerve must expend energy to repair itself, change its membrane back to its original condition, and recapture its previous salt distribution. Therefore, we see that all aspects of cell irritability and response involve energy changes, and we have now some superficial insight into how these changes come about. In each case we have added more details about the workings of the cell motor.

The only thing that is missing from our picture of present-day knowledge of the cell is clearer and more precise information on its structure. I have left this until the last, because it seemed to me if we first looked at what the cell can do, its working parts would have more meaning in that they could be related to specific structures. This would be completely true if we were certain in each case what were the functions of the structures we actually see; but the whole area of cytology is still very much of a frontier in science. Part of the reason is to be found in the limitations of the light microscope. For the last hundred years it has been possible to make the finest instruments, but because of the long wave lengths of visible light, the magnification and the resolving power are strictly limited. Most of the structures of real interest are too small to observe.

There has, however, been an important new advance in the field of microscopy that has been slowly developing into a tool of great power, power that to a large extent still has to be realized. This is the electron microscope, which makes use of the fact that electrons travel with much shorter wave lengths than light and, therefore, can expose far smaller objects. Since the electrons are not visible, the magnified beam must be recorded on a photographic plate. Even though the microscope has been known for some years, it has not been possible to use it effectively with biological material until recently, for there were great technical problems to surmount, and methods are constantly being improved. For instance, cells must be sliced very thin, and methods for this were slow in being perfected. Most difficult of all was the finding of satisfactory ways of drying or fixing the cells so they could be placed in the vacuum chamber necessary for electron microscope photographs and still not show impossible distortions. While these methods undoubtedly will go through many more revolutionary improvements, the results available today give a fascinating new picture of cell structure (Figure 1).

On the visible structural level all we have said so far is that there is a nucleus surrounded by cytoplasm, particles in the cytoplasm, and a binding membrane. On the invisible chemical level we have shown that there are a huge number of different kinds of chemicals all performing a variety of tasks. The question now is to try to see to what extent we can bring these two worlds of different magnitudes together.

While the power of the electron microscope is great, it can only reveal the largest molecules. These are known to be proteins, and, therefore, this is the only chemical constituent that can very easily be identified without further experimental evidence; and even this is only true for the largest proteins. It is possible to see but a few of the 200 million-million molecules, and it is exceedingly difficult to identify the chemical composition of what one does see. The principal approach is to make a comparison between the structures

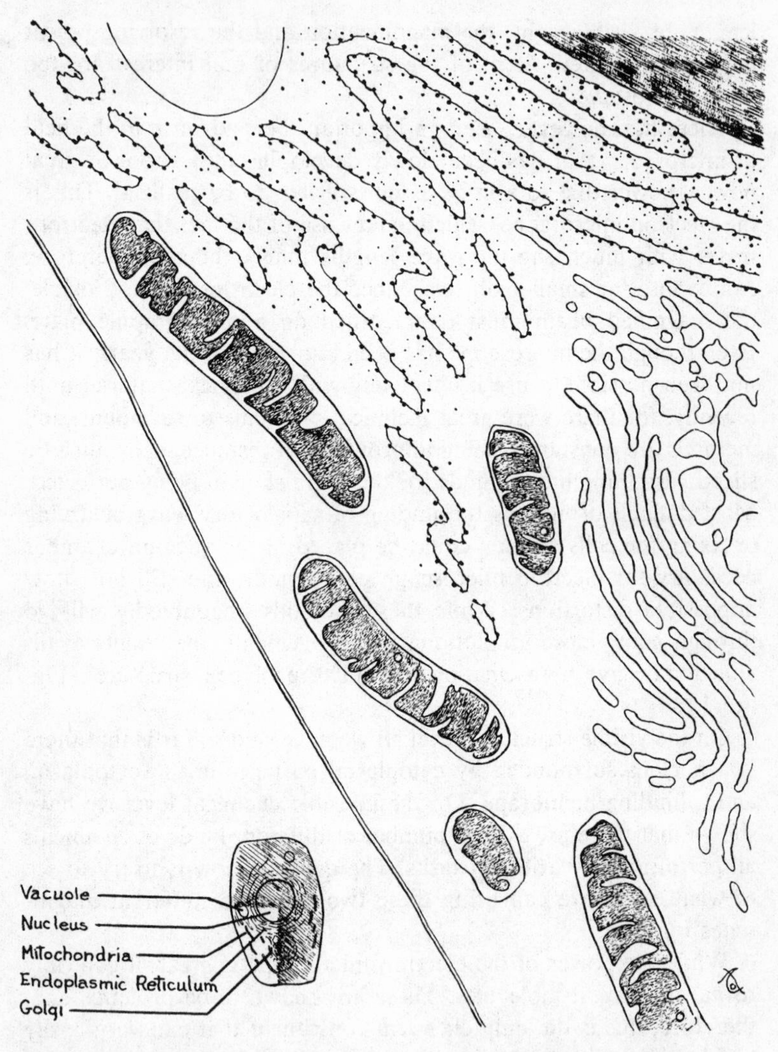

Fig. 1 A diagram of a cell. The relative sizes of the small cell on the lower left and the portion of the large one on the upper right illustrate the difference in magnification and resolution between the ordinary light microscope and the electron microscope, respectively.

visible in intact cells and the structures isolated by chemical fractionation that can both be seen and identified chemically. It is also possible to stain the cell constituents with stains that identify specific substances, and by observing the localization of these stains within the cell it is possible to correlate structures with specific substances.

Beginning with the outside cell membrane one can see that it is exceedingly thin and in most cells very simple in construction. In plants this membrane is, of course, surrounded by a cellulose wall where the orientation of the cellulose is visible by electron microscopy. In some specialized cells, such as red blood cells, the contents of the cells can be removed without damaging the membrane, and these so-called "ghosts" have been analyzed chemically and microscopically. It turns out that they are a matrix of proteins and lipides (a variety of fats), and these substances are to considerable extent responsible for what kind of substances may or may not pass through the membrane.

The most conspicuous and best-known particle within the cytoplasm is the mitochondrion, which in an electron micrograph appears as a sausage-shaped body riddled with folding membranes that form a network of tubes or, more often, flat plates. One of the important advances in recent years is the knowledge that these mitochondria are storehouses of enzymes, kinds of independent units of enzyme activity. They can be isolated by different means and studied chemically, and it is known that they contain many of the basic chains of enzymes responsible for the burning of food. On the one hand, they have the enzymes capable of taking in molecular oxygen, which is used in the combustion process, and they also contain the enzymes for the breakdown of the fuel molecules. They are small enzyme factories that float about the cell. The fact that they have such regular internal structure emphasizes that it is not enough to have a bag full of substances and enzymes capable of attacking the substances. Such a chaotic solution would not properly undergo a steady metabolism despite the controlling influence of the enzymes themselves. Just as in a factory, especially a complex one with an assembly line, it would be hopeless to have all the parts and all the skilled workers scattered at random throughout the factory building; they must be in their proper places so the product can be put together in its proper sequence. The structure of mitochondria and in fact the structure of all parts of the cell is a further assurance that the chemical steps not only go slowly rather than explosively but also go in the proper sequence.

The green plastids of plants that contain the chlorophyll closely resemble mitochondria (except that they are much larger), and they undoubtedly are related. Their function, photosynthesis, which has already been touched upon, is also metabolic. They are another kind of enzyme factory and the only real difference is that the raw materials they use and the product they make differ. Plants, of course, also have mitochondria that can use the sugars manufactured by the plastids.

One of the particularly interesting new discoveries is the presence of delicate double membranes that interlace the cytoplasm. This so-called endoplasmic reticulum is perhaps the closest thing we have to the old hypothesis that there is a "cytoskeleton" within the cell. This reticulum is lined by a series of small dots in electron micrographs, and it is known from recent studies that these dots consist of RNA (ribonucleic acid) and protein. This means that the reticulum is likely to be a region of protein synthesis. Another intriguing observation is that the size and spacing of the endoplasmic reticulum exactly correspond to those of the nuclear membrane; and in some places the two are continuous, and the hypothesis has been proposed that this is a connecting link between the chemical information stored in the nucleus and the production of specific proteins in the cytoplasm. There is also good evidence that the nuclear membrane is perforated by pores providing an additional possible easy route of communication between nucleus and cytoplasm.

The study of the structure of the chromosomes has so far been a disappointment in electron microscopy. No doubt the difficulty is in the fixation methods, and we may hope for progress along those lines. The best pictures of chromosomes come from light microscope studies of the giant chromosomes in the organs of certain flies, but it is known that these chromosomes have been distorted by abnormal growth. In any event they have a banded structure, and it is possible through chemical tests to show that they contain a mixture of DNA (desoxyribonucleic acid) and protein. There is also in nuclei a smaller body called the nucleolus that does not seem to have much structure but appears more as a sac of homogeneous substance, and it is known to be rich in RNA.

Besides the structures mentioned there are a host of others. For instance, there are a number of other small particles found in the cytoplasm, but they have not been discussed, because their metabolic role is obscure (*e.g.,* Golgi bodies). There are also various structures that are not directly related to cell chemistry, as, for example, cilia, the basal bodies of cilia, and the centrioles (which play a key role in cell division). This does not mean that the analysis of their structure has not been interesting and rewarding; quite to the contrary, for some of these structures have been particularly suited to electron microscopy. It is only that here we have confined ourselves to the more basic structure and activity of the cell engine itself.

In concluding this discussion of the cell it may be said that there are many mysteries still to be solved by the experimental biologist. It is presently and will continue for some time to be a field of active research. What we do know gives a picture of an exceedingly complex chemical machine with many parts, many controls, many stabilizing devices. It can maintain itself indefinitely; it can replace lost parts by synthesis; and it can even grow and make more of itself. When it reaches a certain size it will divide by cell division, and each daughter cell will have the constituents of the mother cell. Even the genes on the chromosomes will be exactly duplicated in the mitotic process. All of this seems especially remarkable when one thinks of how small a cell is and what difficulty we have in deciphering even large machines that have just a few of the properties of cell machines.

CHAPTER 2

EVOLUTION

The cell is really such an astoundingly clever unit that when we think of it from the point of view of evolution it seems easier to imagine a single cell evolving into complex animals and plants than it does to imagine a group of chemical substances evolving into a cell. It is very likely that the first step was more difficult, but unfortunately we have no way of checking the matter, for the events leading to a cell have certainly left no record that we can detect on the surface of the earth. The study of early evolution really amounts to educated guesswork. This has the great disadvantage that ultimately we will never be able to prove one hypothesis right and the the other wrong; to some this may seem an advantage for it means no possible check to endless discussion and argument.

Rather than enter into speculations on the origin of life, I shall present a few facts of what we know about possible, living precellular fossils. There is a great danger here also, because we cannot be sure that these examples really are living fossils; they may well be some kind of degeneration of true cells that only give the appearance of being precursors or steps on the road to the evolution of the cell. But whether they are legitimate evolutionary steps or whether they represent some specialized degeneration product of established cells is not really too important in the present context, because they nevertheless illustrate how parts of a cell or a simplified cell can exist and function.

The first example (and the least likely to be a cell precursor, as will soon be evident) is that of viruses. A virus is really part of a cell that can exist independently; it is as though our brains or our heart could exist alone. They are made up primarily of a mixture of protein and nucleic acids. They can be crystallized and stored in this solid state for long periods of time. If they are brought into the presence of a specific living cell that they can invade, then they enter and rapidly multiply by duplication so that one particle will suddenly spring into a million at the expense of the cell that harbors it. In other words viruses are parasites, and many human diseases, including poliomyelitis, are viral in nature.

The point of particular importance with viruses is that they cannot themselves convert energy, yet they need energy in order to duplicate themselves. By entering a cell they can shunt the cell's energy to themselves, rapidly reproduce, and, usually, kill the cell. There are no known instances of a virus duplicating in the absence of a cell despite repeated attempts to demonstrate this, and here lies the reason we suspect viruses are not living fossils but more recently evolved cell parasites.

The fact that in ordinary cells the genic material in the chromosomes is made up of nucleic acids has for a long time suggested that viruses may be some kind of package of free genes. This matter will be discussed further when we come to the subject of genetics; but here it is enough to say that there are many suggestive bits of evidence for this hypothesis. Among other things it is now possible to study the genetics of viruses themselves, and they carry and transmit genetic information in ways that are not totally unlike the methods of higher plants and animals.

A better example of precell living fossils is found in bacteria. It must be recognized that bacteria are conventionally considered cells; but if they are examined closely with either a light microscope or, better, with an electron microscope, it can be seen that they have many fundamental differences from the kind of cell we have already discussed. To begin they are on the whole smaller than all other cells. Their nucleus, while it contains nucleic acids, does not show the characteristic chromosome structure of higher cells. They lack anything resembling mitochondria or an endoplasmic reticulum. They do have particles, but these are exceedingly small. Their cell division appears to be accompanied by a simple pinching in two of the nuclear material rather than any true mitosis. Even their flagella are structurally much less complex than those of ordinary cells (Figure 2).

Nevertheless, as far as energy machines are concerned they are as remarkable if not more so than higher cells. They have a large array of possible different diets; depending on the species, they can use all sorts of fuels. Besides using carbohydrates, fats, and proteins (and in some cases rather difficult forms of these substances, such as cellulose), some species can derive energy from photosynthesis and some from the oxidation of sulfur, iron, methane gas. There are even some that use molecular hydrogen and oxidize it to water. Since the first problem in evolution is one of devising an efficient system of harnessing energy, we may say that bacteria have evolved numerous successful methods of doing this.

As far as their enzyme systems are concerned, they closely parallel larger cells. One of the most interesting things that has been discovered recently is that many of the enzyme reactions that ordinarily appear on the surface of the mitochondrion occur on the cell membrane in bacteria. There was an old and never well-regarded hypothesis that mitochondria are nothing but bacteria that have become permanent parasites in the cytoplasm of large cells. From chemical and electron microscope studies the improbability of this hypothesis is confirmed, but now a new possibility is suggested. The mitochondria are functionally equivalent to the bacterial surface, and if bacteria are precursors to true cells, then the folded mitochondria must be derived from the old cell surface, as though parts of the surface, with special batteries of enzymes, became detached so that they could wander freely into the inside of the cell. True cells are larger, and it is conceivable that more enzyme surface was necessary for the increase in size. The first step in this increase was local convolutions of the bacterial surface and next their detachment to the inside. If this hypothesis is correct, it means that in this evolutionary step there has been a division of labor and an increase in the complexity of parts to meet the demands of increased size.

Another indication of the primitive nature of bacteria is found in their genetic mechanisms. Briefly, there seem to be two kinds of

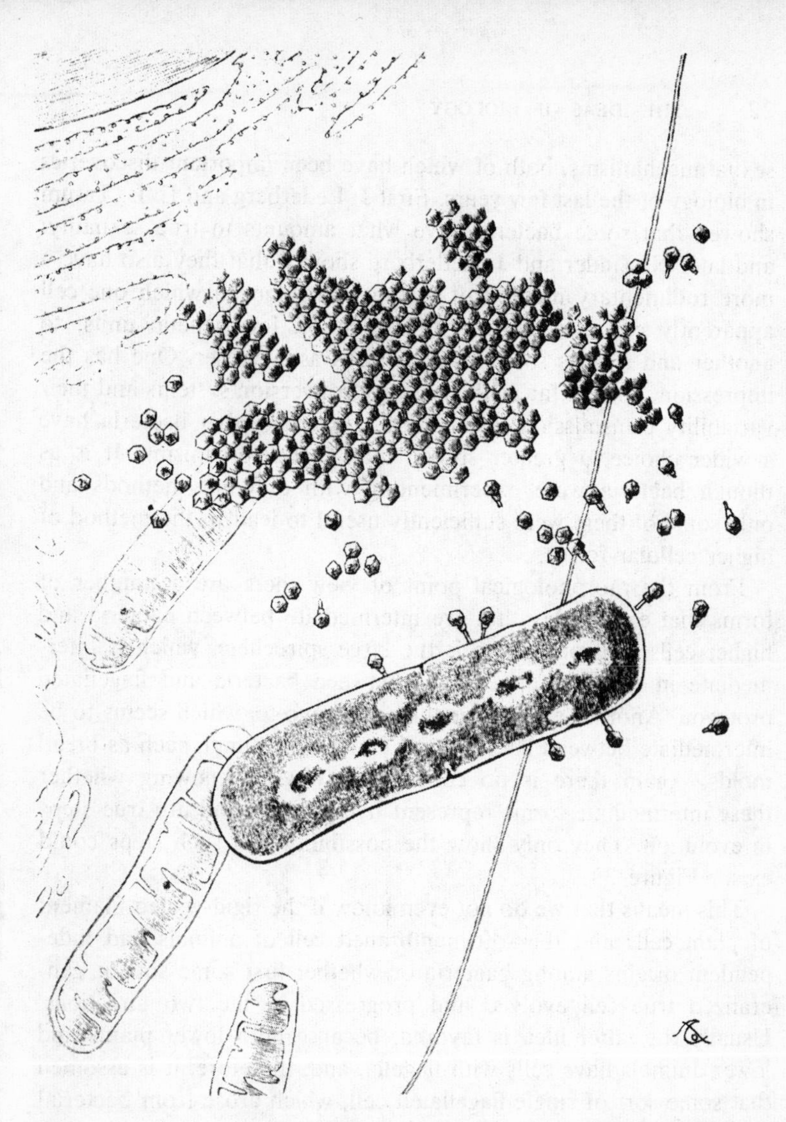

Fig. 2 A drawing based upon electron micrographs of a rod-shaped bacterium in the center and different types of virus particles above. An ordinary cell is shown in the background to give an idea of the relative sizes. Note that the bacterium is a thin section preparation and it is possible to see the beginning of division indicated by the indenting of the cell wall. Also the "nuclear" nodes are evident down the center of the bacterium.

sexual mechanisms, both of which have been important discoveries in biology of the last few years. First J. Lederberg and E. L. Tatum showed that some bacteria have what amounts to true sexuality; and later N. Zinder and J. Lederberg showed that they also have a more rudimentary method of mixing characters in which one cell apparently can contribute a few genes, a few genetic units, to another and it does so by using a virus as a carrier. One has the impression, both as far as their energy conversion systems and their variability transmission systems are concerned, that bacteria have a wider choice, a greater spread than higher organisms. It is as though bacteria were experimenting with different methods and only some of them were sufficiently useful to lead to the method of higher cellular forms.

From the morphological point of view there are a number of forms that exist today that are intermediate between bacteria and higher cells. For one, there is the large spirochete, which is intermediate in size and appearance between bacteria and flagellated protozoa. Another example is the actinomycete, which seems to be intermediate between bacteria and filamentous fungi, such as bread molds. Again there is no conceivable way of knowing whether these intermediate forms represent living fossils and are true steps in evolution. They only show the possibility that such steps could exist (Figure 3).

This means that we do not even know if the rigid-walled filament of plant cells and the soft-membraned cell of animals had independent origins among bacteria or whether first some sort of generalized true cell evolved and progressed in the two directions. Usually the latter idea is favored, because both lower plants and lower animals have cells with flagella, and, therefore, it is assumed that some sort of single flagellated cell, which arose from bacterial ancestors, became the progenitor of all plants and animals. Another factor in favor of this notion is the great similarity between the nuclei and cytoplasmic structures of higher plants and animals as has already been emphasized. The only major difference is the presence of plastids and the associated function of photosynthesis in plants. But in present-day flagellates there are both green and colorless forms that either photosynthesize or sop up organic matter

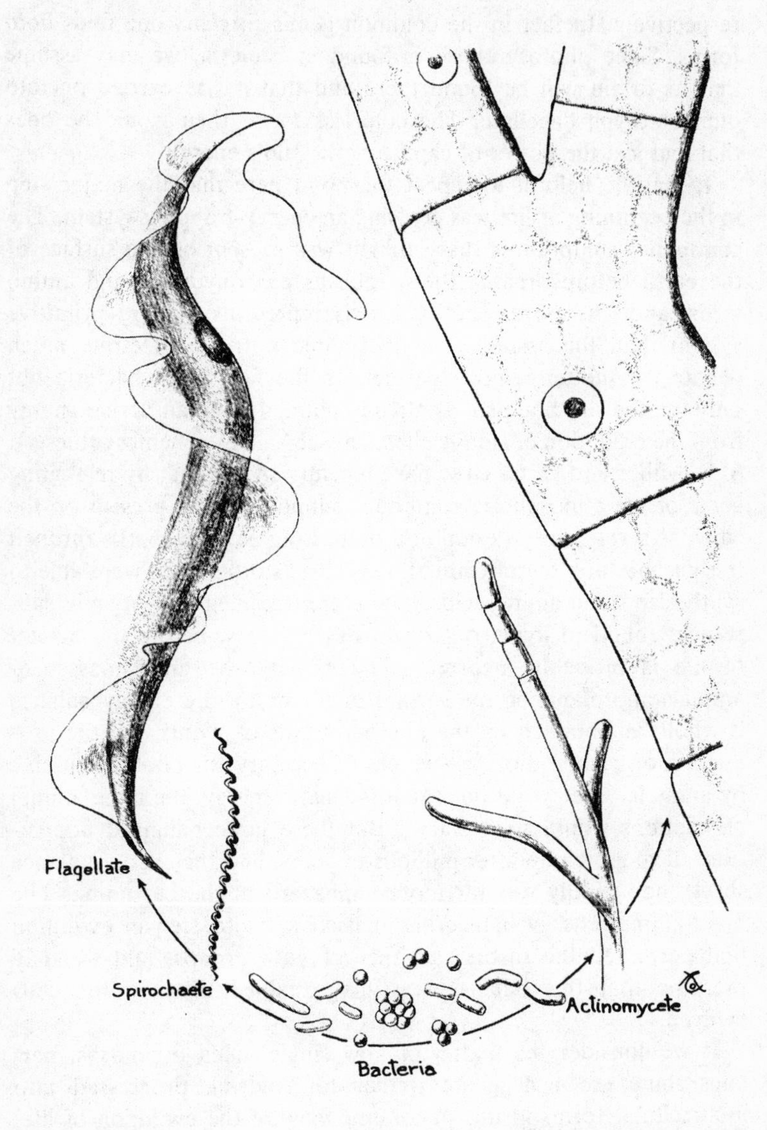

Fig. 3 Various lower forms possibly related to bacteria. Each one is drawn to scale to show the relative sizes.

respectively. In fact in the common genus *Euglena* one finds both forms. Since photosynthesis is found in bacteria, we may assume that its origin will be found there and that it was carried on into our prototype flagellate. The colorless forms then would be ones that had lost the power of capturing the sun's energy.

It may be helpful to repeat the point here that the major step in the beginning of life was devising an energy-trapping system. The common assumption is that sunlight was present on the surface of the earth before organic fuels, such as carbohydrates and amino acids, and, therefore, photosynthesis represents a more primitive system than the assimilation of organic nutrients. Despite much debate the matter is not clear-cut. In the first place bacteria not only use the sun but also, as already pointed out, can derive energy from the oxidation of simple chemical substances (chemosynthesis). S. L. Miller and H. C. Urey have recently shown that by recreating some of the atmospheric conditions supposed to be present on the earth at a very early period and by passing electric sparks through this gas mixture, thereby imitating electric storms, they were able to synthesize some amino acids. Therefore, the idea that organic substances found in living organisms did not exist before the advent of life is probably incorrect. Today, with the great masses of animals and plants on the surface of the earth, the energy balance is wholly maintained by the photosynthesis of plants and the production of carbon dioxide (which is necessary for photosynthesis) by animals. If they did not catch the sun's energy, the huge animal populations would soon starve. But these large balanced populations have grown up after millions of years, and the energy balance sheet undoubtedly was far more haphazard in the beginning. The plant-animal energy balance is in itself a major step in evolution that permitted the further advance of both groups, and we may presume that this balance was first established when the cells evolved.

If we consider the matter of how single-celled organisms, perhaps some green flagellate similar to *Euglena,* progressed into multicellular forms in this panoramic view of the evolution of life, we are again limited by the total absence of any fossil record. This great step forward undoubtedly occurred in an aquatic environment, for the vast majority of unicellular and primitive multicellular forms are aquatic, there being only a few highly specialized terrestrial types. But the deposits of the primeval seas have kept no record except for those forms which had hard shells, and they clearly are not steps in any of the main lines towards multicellularity but offshoots. Examples are the calcareous *Foraminifera* and the siliceous *Radiolaria,* whose beautiful shells have through millions of years of sedimentation led to the formation of rock. The surprising thing here is to what extent these forms are fixed and have remained constant for so long. The living Foraminifera and Radiolaria of today are essentially the same as those of the early seas. These are not progressive groups in an evolutionary sense but what might be called successful dead ends; dead ends, because they have not changed appreciably, but successful, because they continue to exist throughout the ages.

Why did single-celled organisms become multicellular? Why is it, if some groups found the unicellular existence so permanently advantageous, that all groups did not stick to it? The answer probably lies in the matter of the increase in size. Larger organisms can do things that are not possible for smaller ones; they live in different ways, and by becoming large a new world with new opportunities opens up. There are new methods of taking in food, new possibilities of locomotion, new physical habitats that can be entered, and many other innovations. The step is full of the same bright prospects (that we shall examine presently) that opened up to more advanced organisms when they discovered land. There was a host of possible ways of living that did not exist before.

It is no wonder then that we find among living, primitive, multicellular organisms a great variety of different and what must have been separate attempts to increase size. The mechanical problems of size increase are considerable, for the organism must still be able to convert energy and reproduce and respond to its environment; and there have been numerous independent experiments to surmount these problems (Figure 4).

Let us first consider a few examples of those attempts at multicellularity that worked to a limited extent but did not give rise to any great evolutionary sequence. They each are successful in the

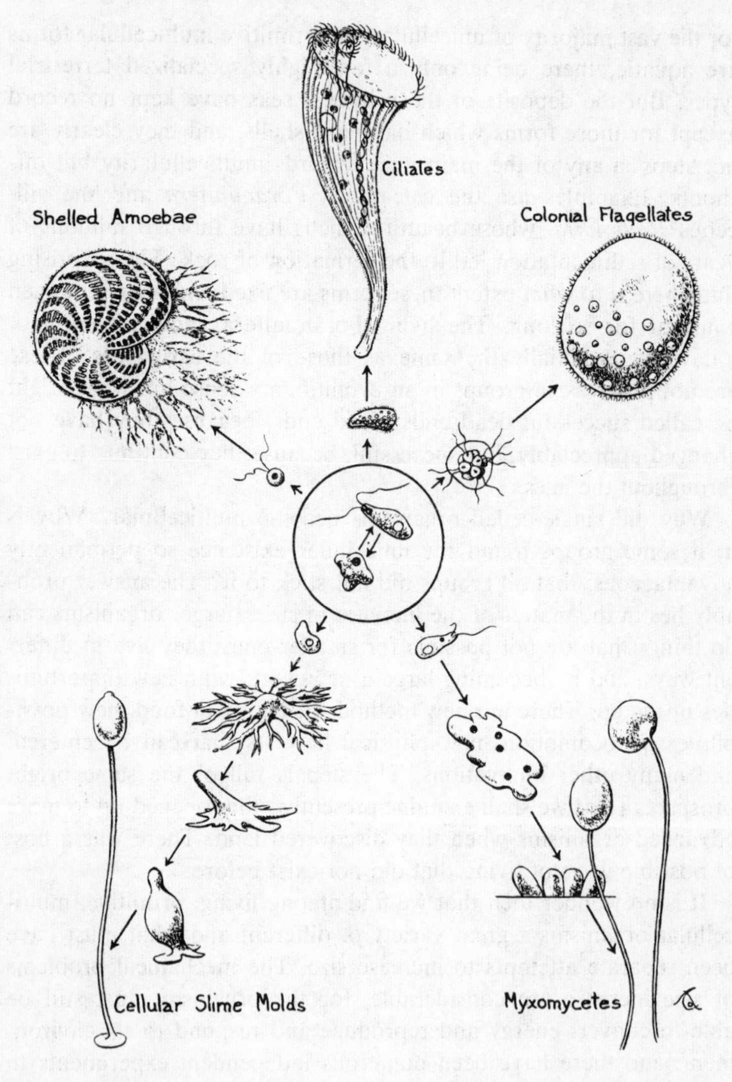

Fig. 4 Some of the different ways of becoming multicellular. The central circle shows the close relationship between a flagellate and an amoeba, both or either of which could have been unicellular ancestors of the surrounding types of organisms.

sense that the organisms live, but they failed as far as progress is concerned.

The ciliate protozoa, of which *Paramecium* is a well-known example, is one attempt, although the method used has only permitted a very slight increase in size. In this case the cytoplasm has been enlarged; but to keep up with the swelling of the cytoplasm, the nucleus has enlarged as well so that instead of having one set of chromosomes the macronucleus of *Paramecium* possesses about two hundred sets. For the chemical activities within the cell this seems to work, although the limit must soon be reached, and one may presume that the reason one does not find paramecia the size of fishes is that a single nucleus in a single mass of cytoplasm of this magnitude would soon have engine trouble. It would be hard for substances to diffuse across great distances to keep the motor going; it would be impossible to achieve any supporting strength in such a large blob of protoplasm; and there would be many other difficulties.

Some other types of primitive organisms, of which the true slime molds or myxomycetes provide a good example, have also tried to keep all the protoplasm within one membrane to make a kind of massive cell; but in this case instead of a giant nucleus there are many nuclei wandering freely about in one very large cytoplasmic sac. The result is that at least the nucleus does not have any problems resulting from increased size; it can operate normally and transfer materials back and forth with the surrounding cytoplasm as before. As a result these slime molds may achieve a far greater size than ciliates, and a large mass of multinucleate cytoplasm might make a heaping tablespoonful although normally it is spread out in a thin layer over the dead branches and leaf mold where it engulfs bacteria and sponges up organic matter. The fact that it spreads thinly emphasizes that its limitation, as far as future evolution and further increase in size is concerned, is not metabolic, as it was for the ciliates; but in this case it is entirely the difficulty of support. A spoonful of protoplasm lacks a certain amount of backbone, and, therefore, what else can it do but hug the ground? As a matter of fact when it does finally fruit, that is, produce spores or seed for the next generation, it divides up into very small units of cytoplasm about a cubic millimeter in size; and each of these (in some species) deposits a small stalk as the small protoplasmic mass rises a millimeter or so into the air. Support can be provided only if the protoplasm is separated into small units.

The more successful method of increase in size is to have a series of cells stuck together in a true multicellular organism. But even this can be done a number of ways: the cells can divide and the daughter products fail to separate, or there can be an aggregation of separate cells. Only the former has given rise to higher animals and plants while the latter is found, for instance, in a curious group of organisms called the cellular slime molds. Here amoebalike cells grow first, and these aggregate into cell masses after they have finished feeding. The cell mass undergoes a series of transformations, with the end result that some of the cells manufacture a supporting stalk, and the remaining cells, which turn into spores, are lifted into the air at the end of the stalk. But their limitations are obvious, for not only is their size small (they do not extend much over a centimeter in height, and they are very slender), but also they must take in their energy, that is, eat, as single cells, which means that they must wait until after dinner before they can become multicellular. They have not been fortunate enough to devise a method of eating while multicellular, and for this reason alone they are an evolutionary blind alley. The multicellular forms that arise by the daughter cells' adhering to one another have to eat while they grow to provide the energy for synthesis, and having solved this problem they can successfully achieve greater evolutionary advancement.

The green cells that have become multicellular find no difficulty at all in constantly feeding during growth; for, after all, they need only to keep their chlorophyll where the sun can reach it and to be in the presence of some carbon dioxide. They would seem to be ideally suited in this regard for multicellularity. The plant cells that are colorless and lack the photosynthetic machinery, such as the filamentous fungi, must be near a rich supply of dissolved food substances that they can drink in through their cell walls and cell membranes. The animal cells that feed on particles have a more severe evolutionary step to make, for if a mass of cells is to obtain food effectively, it must have some sort of communal food processing or gut system. The sponges have solved this one way by making an elaborate canal system in which the water is moved by flagellar motion, and the collar cells that line the canals can individually remove the food particles from the water. In coelenterates, for example, in *Hydra,* we have the beginnings of a true gut system, with a mouth and digestive enzymes that pour into the gut cavity. But certainly these solutions of sponges and coelenterates of the animal feeding problem are far more complex than the photosynthetic solution, and, indeed, as J. R. Baker (who originated this argument) points out, this provides a simple explanation as to why there are so many different types of primitive multicellular plants and so few primitive multicellular animals.

If we make the reasonable but totally unsubstantiated hypothesis that a flagellate is the ancestor of all multicellular forms, we see that there have been a number of attempts that have run into blind alleys (only a few of which were discussed here) while two of the attempts have seemed successful—the one that leads to higher plants and the one that leads to higher animals. We are, of course, always assuming that the present day unsuccessful attempts are either living fossils or that they parallel types of organisms that did live in an early period of earth history. The idea is that unicellular flagellates performed a number of different experiments, and, while each is interesting and even stable in its own right, only two were capable of forward progression. The fact that there are two might not be, as was already implied, a chance occurrence; for neither plants alone nor animals alone could have flourished the way they now do if only one existed and not the other. Through the exchange of organic substances provided by plants and carbon dioxide provided by animals, these two great kingdoms of organisms can keep one another supplied. If all the plants in the world were wiped out in one day, all the animals would be dead in the next few, except for the carnivores and carrion eaters that would have one last, final feast.

Lower plants, with a few sporadic exceptions, have also been poor in leaving any fossil record, and again we are left with the living forms to provide clues so that we can puzzle together the past. This is especially difficult, because each group of lower plants is so remarkably diverse that it is difficult and, indeed, dangerous to attempt any definite evolutionary sequence. Therefore, it might be more useful, rather than stressing the genealogy, to stress the diversity of forms and habitats, to show how the lower plants have taken advantage of different environments and conquered new worlds.

The algae comprise a very large and heterogeneous group. They include many single-celled forms (such as diatoms) and a number of related multicellular forms. These may range from single filaments, as in *Spirogyra,* to huge and massive seaweeds, such as the giant kelp. (It used to be said that these were the largest of all plants, and reports for their length ranged from 600 to 1,500 feet. In point of fact the record is a mere 138 feet, but still this is no small plant.) The algae are subdivided into a series of groups depending upon their color, their pigments; and there are blue-green, green, golden, brown, and red algae. These groupings are meaningful, in fact so much so that each group is only very remotely related, if at all, to the others. The most likely relation lies between the primitive blue-green algae (of which *Oscillatoria* is an example) and the complex and elaborate red algae, for they both have similar pigments, and they both lack any motile stages in any phases of their life history (Figure 5).

The brown algae, which are largely marine, provide the giant forms. Even though this group is undoubtedly not a precursor to higher plants, it can hardly be claimed that they are a blind alley, for even though they have their ultimate limitations, they did make great strides of progress. Their large size is, of course, mainly possible because they have remained aquatic and, therefore, do not need any very specialized system of support. (The consistency of larger kelp is something like that of a garden hose.) But size alone creates another problem that they have effectively met. In the first place their bulk requires an efficient sun-catching device for photosynthesis, and secondly the products of photosynthesis must be carried to all parts. In the kelp there is a large flat blade that amounts to a huge leaf that floats near the surface of the sea where the sun can

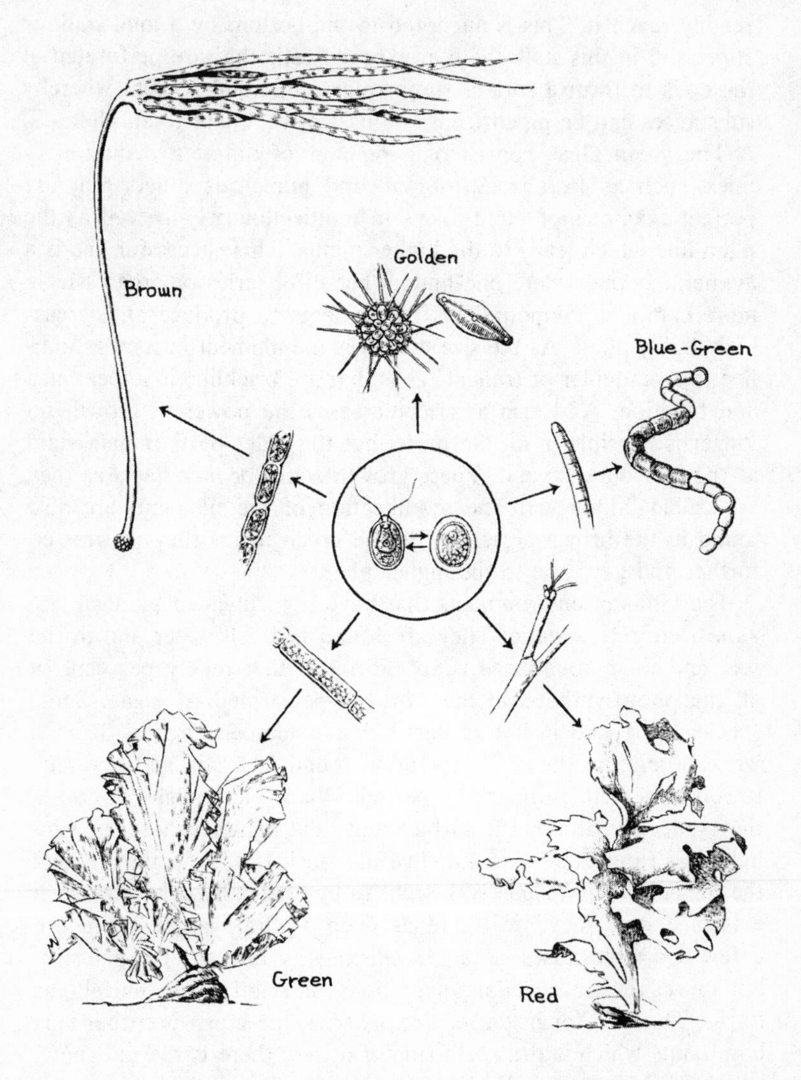

Fig. 5 A variety of different ways of becoming multicellular among the algae. The central circle shows two different stages of a unicellular alga. Presumably these are the ancestors of flagellated colonies, simple filamentous forms, and the larger marine algae.

readily reach it. This is anchored to the bottom by a long stalk or stipe, and in this stalk there are special cells that are perforated at the ends to form a sort of rudimentary plumbing system whereby substances can be piped from one part of the plant to another.

The green algae consist of a number of different evolutionary lines, such as *Volvox, Spirogyra,* and numerous others that are perfect examples of blind alleys in multicellularity, as well as the main line which leads to the higher plants. This successful line is a filamentous one where one finds a beautiful series of progressively more complex compoundings of filaments to produce an increasingly bulky plant. As the size increases the filament becomes modified to rectangular or truncate cells that are bricklike in appearance and function. And also as size increases the power of growth no longer is possible in all the parts; but the older parts remain rigid as the new ones expand. These growth zones or *meristems* as they are called, along with the modification of the filament, are also found in the brown algae, but in the green forms they progressed further and gave rise to the higher plants.

The kinds of environments that have been invaded by algae are almost entirely aquatic. They are found in fresh water and in the sea, and their abundance is so enormous that ninety per cent of all the photosynthesis in the world is performed by algae. Some species are found in hot springs living at temperatures of 85° C., while others are the only vegetation found in arctic and antarctic regions where there might be periodic thaws. Although in the sea they generally occupy the surface and tidal regions where the sunlight is strong, they also can live at considerable depths. In fact the pigment of red algae is thought to be especially suited for such existence, and they are found as deep as 200 yards. There are a few scattered cases of algae existing as terrestrial organisms, but the cases are peculiar adaptations of small, often unicellular forms. There is, for instance, *Protococcus,* the green fuzz that tells boy scouts which is the north side of a tree; there is the red snow, which is a small alga that grows on the surface of old snow; and a final example could be the curious red alga that lives in the hair of the three-toed sloth. The algae themselves, considered as a whole, have not successfully coped with a terrestrial existence, but the important thing is that they are the progenitors of the truly terrestrial forms that are the higher plants.

The conquest of land was the major event in the evolution of plants. Here was a better place in the sun for photosynthesis and no competition from other forms. It was a land of opportunity. The simple bryophytes, particularly the mosses, remained so small and kept to such moist places that, as a first step, the problems imposed by an existence in air were approached cautiously. Support was no great problem because of their size, and drying-out was prevented by the immediate high humidity.

But for complete success, for complete conquest, here is what was needed: A system to prevent or control water loss that is found ultimately in the impervious, waxy cuticle and the controlled openings or stomata; a system of support that is the formation of fibers in the vascular bundle; water and salts both of which can be tapped by a root system in the ground; an effective sun-trapping system that is found both in the internal and external construction of a leaf; a system of transport of water, salts, and the products of photosynthesis that is found in the elaborate vascular system, which includes the pipes of both the internal wood or xylem and the external bast or phloem. As soon as the first truly vascular plants appeared on the crust of the earth, good fossil records remained, and so we know that all these progressive specializations to land existence were accompanied by a general trend of increase in size. *Protococcus* is terrestrial, yet it has none of the problems of a large terrestrial plant. Size and existence on land have created the need for these adaptive changes. Even the growth pattern of higher plants, with their highly organized growth zones, is tied up with these two factors (Figure 6).

The sequence of groups of vascular plants and their period of climax in early earth history are well known and established. In brief and without giving a single detail, there is a steady sweep up through the pteridophytes (ferns and horsetails), the lycopods, the gymnosperms, and the angiosperms. For a period each of these earlier groups was master and ruled the forests of the earth. They achieved great size and in all ways seemed perfection. Why then did one group succeed the other as the dominant form of vegeta-

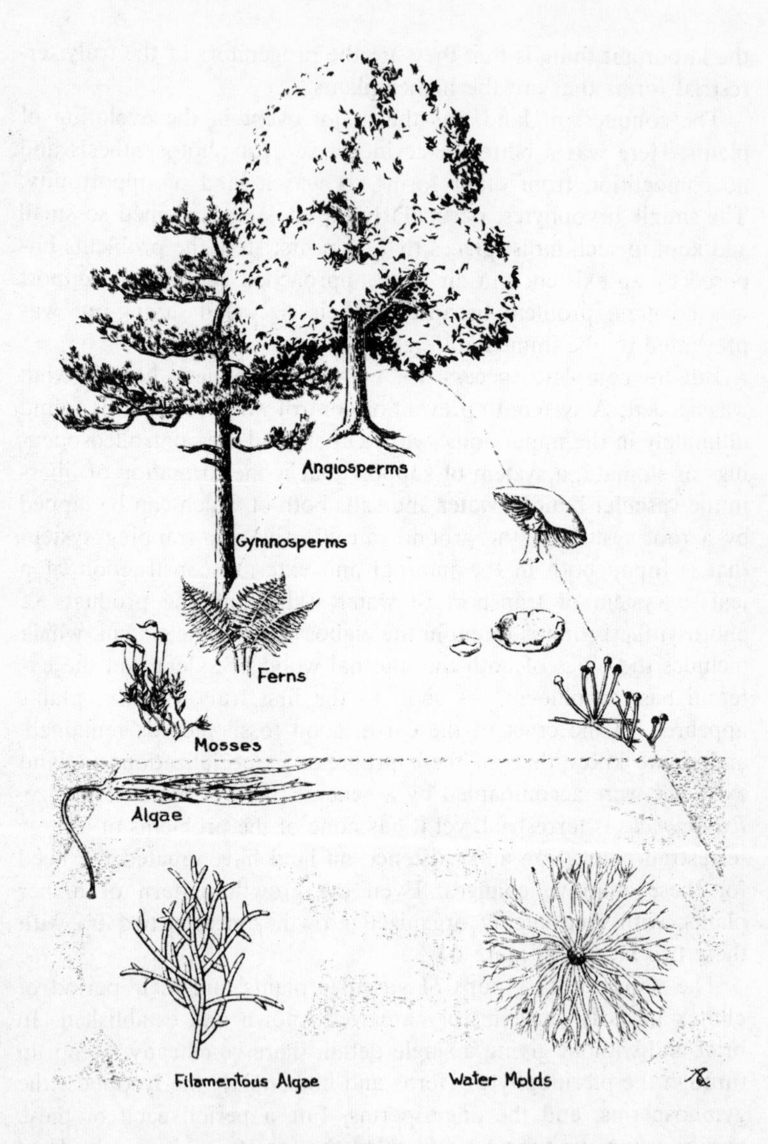

Fig. 6 Plant evolution and conquest of land. On the left there are the major groups of green plants, while on the right there is the independent conquest of land by the fungi.

tion; what produced the new change; what do angiosperms and, to a lesser extent, gymnosperms possess that makes them so prevalent in the world today?

The answer undoubtedly lies primarily in the fact that while the ferns or any of the other earlier groups were effective in coping with a particular environmental situation, they gave rise to forms that were even more so. In competition—and competition is involved here—small changes may give large advantages in the struggle for existence.

If we look to see the nature of the changes that occurred in the vascular plants, we see for one that there is a slow and steady improvement of the structure of the plants: the root system becomes more effective, then the supporting system, the transport system, the photosynthetic system; all of these increase in efficiency. Perhaps one of the more notable improvements has been in the reproductive system. In ferns fertilization takes place in the delicate, algal-like gametophyte (the prothallus), which is dependent upon a damp, boggy spot for growth; and since the sperm is motile, this phase of the life cycle is still aquatic. Only the adult fern, which results from fertilization, can live in dry air. No doubt this fact explains why ferns are not found in the desert. The club mosses have improved matters somewhat by holding the gametophyte in a spore case so that it need not depend upon moisture for growth, although again fertilization cannot take place without water. The gymnosperms are the first to successfully achieve what might be called dry fertilization. In the primitive *Ginkgo* the sperm is still motile, but this is a superfluous and useless hangover from the past. In conifers the sperm is now pollen and can be carried by the wind. The gametophyte never leaves the plant; it is held safely within the cones so that external water is not needed for any of the reproductive steps. The same is, of course, true in angiosperms where there have been numerous further refinements for bringing the pollen to the egg. Besides taking advantage of the wind, the use of colorful, scented nectar-bearing flowers to attract pollen-carrying insects and birds shows how remarkable some of the devices, some of the evolutionary steps may be.

With these attributes and many others modern plants today have essentially gained greater independence of their environment; they can live in a greater variety of places; they do not always have to exist in a bog. We find plants in the desert, in the high mountains, and in the extreme northern and southern cold regions. There are reversions to aquatic life, and higher plants are found floating on the surface, like duckweed, or submerged, like *Elodea* and many others. Plants can even grow on other plants, not only as parasites, like mistletoe, but simply using the large plant as an attachment as do orchids and Spanish "moss." In each conquest of a new habitat there are secondary changes that have occurred, and, for instance, desert plants have devised a series of special devices for conserving water.

If we take a final glance at the panorama of the evolution of plants, there are two impressive lessons in this story of persistent change. There is a constant pressure to find new environments and exploit them; and secondly, once they are conquered, there is a constant competition to find the most efficient and effective form that can dominate the particular environment. This results in one group after another winning out in the competition and reaching the dominant position in succession. Presently when we examine the mechanism of evolution, we will be able to say more about the nature of these competitive changes.

Before leaving plants and turning to the animals, a footnote should be added for the fungi. These organisms are clearly an offshoot of the main plant evolutionary sequence to angiosperms, but, nevertheless, in their own progression they show some interesting parallels to the green plants. For one, some of the fungi have become terrestrial, and even though a high humidity is usually necessary, some will rise into the air for a fair distance, as, for example, the larger mushrooms. In these cases there are specific adaptations geared to an existence on land, such as a loss of motility in the reproductive cells and fertilization taking place by filament tips of opposite sexes meeting and fusing. This is shown strikingly when one compares the closely related water molds (aquatic Phycomycetes) and the terrestrial bread molds (terrestrial Phycomycetes, *e.g., Mucor* or *Rhizopus*). The fungi are a large and highly successful group that have invaded many new environmental niches, often ones that are unavailable to green plants because of their different mode of nutrition. Since they do feed on dissolved substances, it is also not surprising that many of them should have become parasites.

If we now turn to the animal kingdom, we will be impressed by the totally different forms and functions of the organisms involved, yet there are some striking parallels in their evolutionary changes. Again in the more primitive forms the fossil record is poor and confusing, and our ability to reconstruct proper evolutionary sequences is therefore severely limited (Figure 7). It has been a field of almost continuous discussion and argument, and even today there are numerous views as to which are the most primitive multicellular animals, all of which are insecurely founded upon guesswork, opinion, and tradition or the opposing of tradition.

One view, which has received its principal stimulus from the work of Hadzi, favors the idea that the complex ciliate protozoa (*e.g., Paramecium*) gave rise to the acoel flatworms, and these in turn are the stem of all higher forms. These flatworms are extremely simple in their construction; they are covered with a layer of cilia, and inside they have no cell membranes but merely a multinucleate mass of protoplasm. Presumably the higher cellular forms came into being as a result of the nuclei becoming compartmentalized at a later stage. Certainly one does find a close relation between these acoel worms and the higher flatworms such as *Planaria*.

The loyal opposition (for which I must confess some sympathy) objects to the above on a number of grounds, especially the fact that these acoel flatworms have a complex, cellular embryology involving regular cell cleavages, and they only assume their noncellular condition as they approach maturity. This is quite unlike anything found in ciliates and suggests that the ancestors of the acoels might have been a more complex cellular form and that the acoels have undergone a degeneration. The alternative is for the flagellate protozoa to have produced directly some kind of colonial organism (and a number of simple flagellate colonies exist today) that ultimately gave rise to three groups: to the sponges, to the coelenterates, and finally to the main line that leads directly to the acoel flatworms. Here there are thought to be two major branches

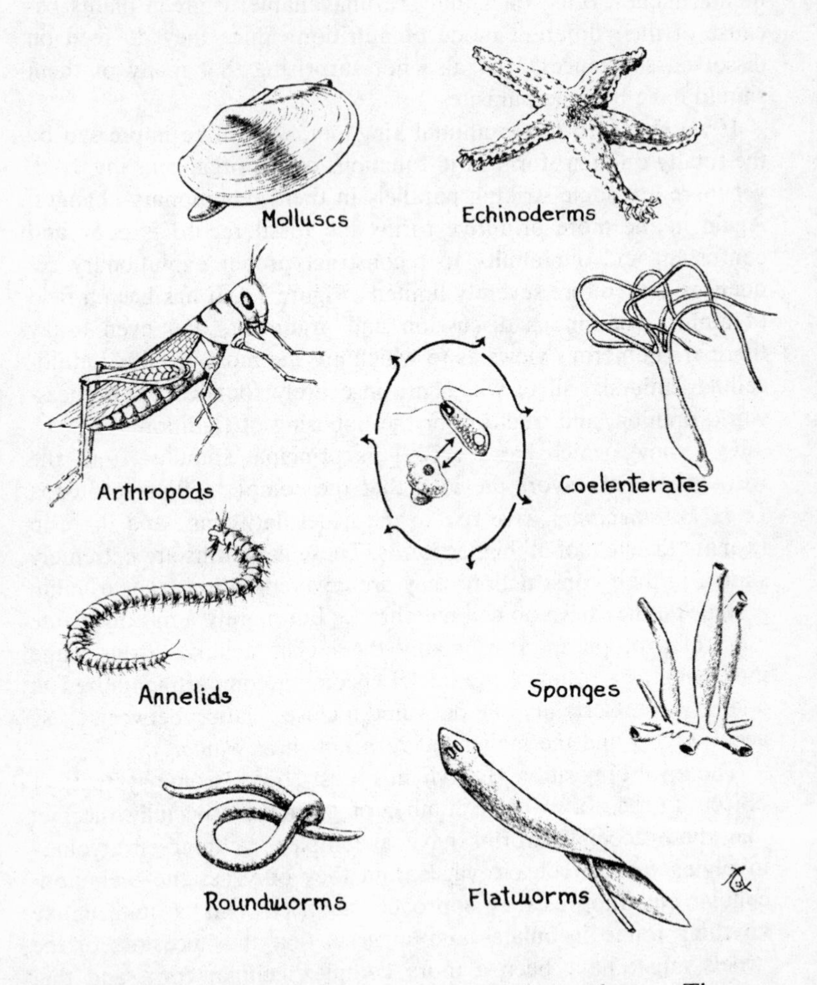

Fig. 7 The major groups of multicellular invertebrates. The ancestral unicellular amoeba and flagellate is again shown in the center. Since the relationships between groups remains largely uncertain and speculative, and since undoubtedly some of the groups arose independently, they are arranged in an indefinite circle rather than in a hypothetical family tree.

in the evolutionary tree: one giving rise to the higher worms (round and annelid worms), the arthropods (Crustacea, insects, and spiders), and the mollusks (snails, clams, and other bivalves, squid, and cuttlefish) and the other branch giving rise to the echinoderms (starfish, sea urchins, etc.), the hemichordates (sea squirts), and finally the chordates.

As with the higher plants, the fossil record of the chordates is excellent, and it is possible to reduce speculation and see a clear-cut evolutionary sequence. With each group there was at least one period, often shortly after its inception, of flowering where there was a rapid expansion both of numbers of species and numbers of individuals. The first group is the jawless fish, of which today we still have some living fossils in the form of hagfish and lamprey eels. The placoderms, fish covered with armor plates, came next and are now wholly extinct. The cartilaginous fish (*e.g.,* sharks) and the bony fish arose next, and both groups remained common and successful until the present. The amphibians (frogs, newts, salamanders, etc.), arose from the primitive bony fish where the fins became transformed into limbs. The crossopterygians or ray-finned fish represent a primitive transition form, and until a few years ago they were thought to be extinct; but to everyone's astonishment one of these fish was caught in a net off the coast of South Africa. Since then a number have been found, and we no longer need to rely on their flattened fossil bones to learn their internal structure (Figure 8).

The amphibians, as their name implies, made the first step towards the conquest of land. All the possibilities of this virgin environment were opened up; and, furthermore, it offered an escape from the competition of the well-populated sea. With a very few exceptions, amphibians are dependent upon water for their reproduction phases. The egg of a frog is laid in the water, and the tadpole is completely aquatic. Gills, which are also used by fish for their oxygen intake, are delicate structures that are directly bathed by the water. If they are brought into air, they will soon dry on their surface and no longer function in trapping oxygen into the blood. In metamorphosis the lungs develop, and oxygen can be obtained directly from the air by the mature frog. By having an

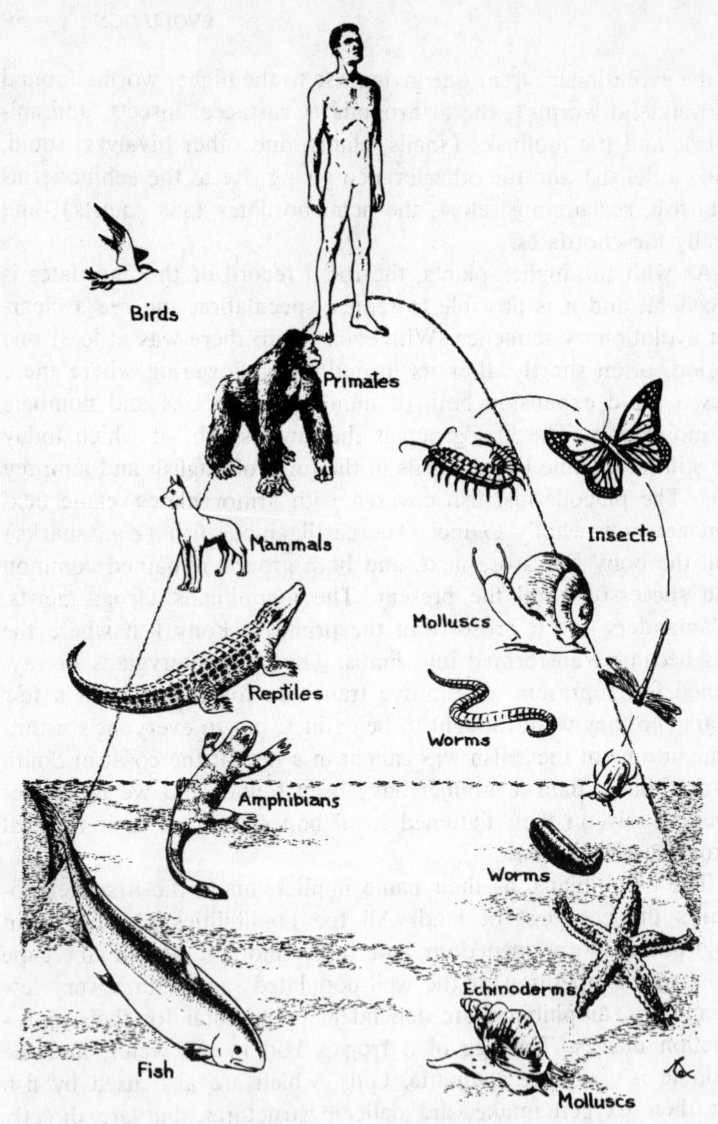

Fig. 8 Animal evolution and the conquest of land and air. The succession of vertebrates is on the left, and similar environmental adaptations have been achieved independently by various invertebrate groups, as shown on the right.

internal cavity, it is possible to keep the air saturated with water vapor so that the living wall of the lung will remain thin and the blood can easily pick up the oxygen. Another problem on land is loss of water through the skin, and some amphibians must keep near water and stay wet; but others have evolved impervious skin (as did plants with their waxy surface), and the adult great horned toad survives even in the desert. The problem of support is somewhat different for animals from what it is for plants, because animals not only have to be propped up, but also they have to move. One of the really remarkable adaptations to new environmental conditions has been the origin and steady improvement of the skeletal system and the limbs of all the higher vertebrates.

The reptiles show the result of the trend toward independence from water. They no longer need water for fertilization where egg and sperm are simultaneously shed into the water; the sperm is directly introduced into the female by internal fertilization. Their eggs are encased in an impervious shell to prevent evaporation, and the young spend all of their very early life within shells so that when they hatch, they can use their lungs directly and never go through a period of gill breathing. Some reptiles even retain the incubating eggs within the mother and give birth to live young (ovoviviparity). Their scaly coats are quite waterproof, and a few lizards are found existing happily in desert environments. Some reptiles, on the other hand, have reverted to the water, and the huge sea turtles spend their whole lives at sea and return to lay their eggs in the hot sand.

The birds exactly duplicate the reptiles as far as internal fertilization and the production of shelled eggs is concerned. They have, however, made two great innovations. They are warm blooded, that is they maintain a constant body temperature independent of the environmental temperature that insures high muscular efficiency even in the coldest weather. Second, they have found yet another world to conquer—the air. By lightening their bone structure, by the alteration of reptilian scales into feathers, and finally by major changes in the bone and muscle shape, they can fly. The air is the environment where they can travel, even migrate from one part of the world to another to follow the seasons and food supply; where they can escape predators; where they can effectively catch their prey, be it an insect, a fish, or a small mammal. Flight has many obvious and wonderful advantages for survival, yet some birds, to meet the demands of a specific environment or a specific set of competitive conditions, have lost it. Ostriches and kiwis are examples of flightless birds that are permanently grounded, and penguins can use their wings only for swimming; they have again become aquatic animals, as were their remote ancestors.

For vertebrates the reproductive phase seems to be the most vulnerable, and we see a constant trend, from the inefficient production of millions of eggs in fish where very few are expected to survive to the increasing protection and care of the young, so that the clutch size is reduced. Part of the reason for this trend is that the complexity of the individuals increases as one goes up the scale, and with this increase there is a longer period of childhood and immaturity, a longer period of needed parental care. This is obvious even on the level of instruction that a parent gives its young; the more advanced the animal, the longer the necessary period of supervised learning.

This trend is seen strikingly in the mammals, which also had their origins in the reptiles. The most primitive mammals, the monotremes (duck-billed platypuses and spiny anteaters) lay eggs. When the young are born the mother has rudimentary mammary glands that provide a nutritious secretion that helps the hatched young; but in effect this is no more of an advance than the crop secretion of pigeons ("pigeon milk") that is regurgitated for the young birds. The marsupials or pouch-bearing mammals (kangaroo, opossum, etc.), on the other hand, have well-developed mammary glands. The egg shell, however, is gone, and the mother keeps the fertilized egg in her womb until it develops into a small fetus (viviparity). This period of gestation is very short, a matter of a few days, and then the minute young climb to the pouch and fix themselves onto the nipples where they continue their growth. In placentals the embryo attaches itself to the uterus wall by means of a placenta and receives its nutrition for an extended period of pregnancy. When it is born into the world, it is already well advanced in its growth and development. It can readily be seen that each step in this progression is one of making reproduction and child raising independent of the environment, in this way improving the chances of survival of any one offspring. Because of their increased complexity, the offspring require more rearing, and, therefore, all these safety measures reduce waste and inefficiency.

Aside from progress in reproduction, mammals have been extremely successful in many other ways, perhaps the most conspicuous of which is the steady improvement of the brain. But mammals also have other structural features that make them into sturdy yet adaptable machines, and they have after a slow start completely supplanted the reptiles as the prime fauna of the earth. They range from the small shrews to the huge elephant, from the sluggish sloths to the alert monkeys, from the flying bats to the wholly aquatic whales and dolphins. Like the higher plants, the angiosperms, they seem to be enjoying a dominant position in the world today.

In a footnote to the discussion of plant evolution we saw that fungi, an offshoot, showed many striking parallels to the main line, such as special adaptations in their own conquest of land. We might add here a series of such postscripts for various groups of invertebrate animals. For instance mollusks have developed ways of breathing on land, as we know from the snails and slugs in our gardens. But the most striking examples are among the insects. By means of the body being perforated with air tubes (tracheae), they have a kind of branching lung; they have beautifully efficient legs for walking; and they have conquered the air in a spectacular fashion. The variety of reproductive methods runs the gamut from aquatic laval stages (*e.g.*, the mosquito) to purely terrestrial development (*e.g.*, the housefly). Their principal limitation seems to be one of size imposed by their exoskeleton, but by being small they do not compete with mammals; they live in a separate size-world.

There are many close similarities between animal evolution and plant evolution. This is seen most impressively in all the steps leading to the conquest of land. In both cases they were faced with probiems of water loss, support in air, and the difficulty of becoming independent of water for reproduction and early development. The environment itself created the problems, and each major kingdom solved the problems in its own way. From a functional point of view the problems are the same, and the only differences in their respective solutions is to be found in their different innate structures: plants in general are relatively immobile, sun-catching energy machines, while animals are mobile machines that require an input of chemical energy.

The purpose of this survey of evolution is to show what kinds of changes have occurred and how the living world we know today emerged from primitive precells. It took many millions of years to occur, but even with this rich supply of time, evolution seems a remarkable process. It used to be thought of as a mysterious process as well, but since the great work of Charles Darwin the mystery has mostly vanished, although the process seems, if anything, more remarkable and more interesting than ever.

Darwin's principle (and it was also discovered independently by Alfred Wallace) is extremely simple. He was impressed by the fact that many organisms give birth to or raise far more offspring than ultimately reach adulthood or reproductive age. All organisms show variation among individuals. The idea is that those variants that are suited to the particular environment survive, and those that are for some reason not well adapted are eliminated. There is a natural selection and a survival of the fittest.

A first caution that should be made concerning this principle is that there is sometimes the implication that all life is in a grim struggle and that progress is only achieved by a deadly competition between individuals. This is not necessarily the case; and, as Darwin himself understood, the real importance lies not in the deaths by competitive fighting but by success in producing offspring that have the kinds of variation that favor survival. What are selected ultimately, therefore, are those individuals which are well adapted.

Another point that should be made about this theory of evolution is really a historical one. Darwin knew that the keystone to his theory was a variation among the offspring and that the variation was in some way inherited. Long after the publication of his *Origin of Species* in 1859, he attempted to understand the nature of this variation; but his attempt was as much a failure as his theory of natural selection was a success. It was Gregor Mendel who discovered the laws of heredity, and although they were published in 1866, they were not recognized and known to the students of evolution and biologists in general until after 1900. This has now become the science of genetics, and as we shall see in the next chapter, it has now been completely welded to the study of evolution.

Here we may mention merely one point that has a bearing on the matter of the significance of natural selection as the over-all principle of evolution. Before the work of Darwin, Lamarck (and certain others since then) favored the idea that evolutionary change came about by use and disuse of parts and that the change acquired in the lifetime of one individual by use or disuse would be inherited in the next. In other words variation was caused by function. While some years ago there were many cogent arguments against this, it was not totally dismembered as a possibility (at least in the form presented) until the genetic studies of this century. It has been shown that while use or disuse may affect the size of an organ in an individual, this change in size is in no way passed on to the offspring. All that the offspring inherit is (1) the initial size of the organ or the parent and (2) the capacity to change the size of the organ by use or disuse. The details of how the variation is controlled can wait, but the fact that this kind of inheritance of acquired character does not occur is an established and firm conclusion.

When Darwin published his book, it created a tremendous sensation; it seemed to be the key for which the whole world was waiting. However, there immediately arose many sharp critics who saw loopholes, and these critics served the useful function of examining all the implications of the theory; this stimulated further work, all of which has made the theory more and more accepted by biologists. In the hundred years since the publication of *Origin of Species,* our opinion of Darwin was never so high as it is now.

The reason for the doubt of the critics is readily understandable. It stems partly from the fact that the theory of natural selection is suspiciously simple to account for the complexities of the structure of animals and plants and their evolution. Consider, for example, the evolution of the cell itself. How, indeed, could selection account for all this intricate machinery?

The answer is that for selection to occur one must have variation and reproduction. In the very earliest beginning of the evolution of a cell it is not clear what came first or how it was put together; but once an energy-converting system was established, the variation could be handled by changes in the nucleic acids (and possibly other chemical constituents), and reproduction could be handled by the synthesis of new substances and the replication of the complex proteins and nucleic acids. Therefore, given this kind of initial mechanism, all that follows in the way of animals and plants must be the result of natural selection. Part of the evidence concerns whether or not variations can be of such a nature that they will provide material for these elaborate progressive changes. Insofar as it is possible to obtain an answer to this question from the genetics of present-day organisms, we will see in the next chapter that there is no reason to suppose there are any serious difficulties. The other part of the evidence concerns whether or not selection really occurs. It is all very well to categorically state that such and such a structure has been perfected by natural selection, but it is another matter to prove that this is so, especially as the change may have taken a million years and many successive generations. Darwin supported his argument by showing that domestic animals can be modified by the selection imposed by man. If only those cows with the highest milk production are bred, the average milk production per cow may show a steady improvement. But this still does not answer the question as to whether this kind of selection occurs normally in nature.

There have been some recent experiments of H. B. D. Kettlewell that bear directly on this point. It is a well-known fact that periodically animals give rise to exceptional offspring that are either white (albinos) and lack all pigment or are dark (melanic) and have an excess of pigment. Usually these forms disappear and do not make up any significant part of the population, but in the last hundred years it was noticed in England and on the continent that there has been a very marked increase in the number of melanic forms of a certain moth. It was noticed that this rise of dark moths paralleled the rise of industrialization, and the hypothesis was made that the dark forms were suddenly favored in natural selection because of their protective coloration in the new, smoky industrial centers (where the melanic forms existed in special abundance). To test the hypothesis Kettlewell took a large number of normal and melanic forms of the moth and placed them (1) on trees in a wooded area far away from a city and (2) in a wood near some factories where the bark was considerably darkened by the soot. These moths, which in the daytime stay still on the tree trunks, are greedily eaten if they can be discovered by a number of different kinds of insectivorous birds. In the remote wood a far greater number of the dark forms were eaten than the better camouflaged normal ones, while in the wood near the factories the lighter normal moths were picked off by the birds and the melanic ones left largely unmolested. This experiment was repeated a number of different ways, all with essentially the same result: this new blackish variant does have a selective advantage in the woods near industrial centers. We have then very clear evidence that natural selection does take place and is an important factor in changing the character of organisms in nature.

Another lesson we may learn from these experiments is that the change in the moth population was a result of the change in environment. In considering this matter we may make a first step in an attempt to understand the factors that cause evolutionary changes. If the environment changes, then clearly what constitutes adaptiveness may itself undergo change. New environments not only provide new opportunities but impose new restrictions, new selective forces. The example of the industrial areas is an extremely simplified instance of this principle; imagine the conquest of land as the other extreme where a new environment is so radically different that the number of new opportunities is great and the selective forces utterly changed.

In the case of industrial melanism the change occurred without any migration on the part of the moth but rather as the result of the somewhat soiled hand of man. Industrialization is a new condition that we have imposed upon the moth's normal environment. In the case of the conquest of land, plants and animals have moved out of their aquatic environment and migrated to a new, virgin environment. Probably the first steps were effected in tidal regions or in damp bogs, but through these transitional areas there eventually was a real transfer to land. With the transfer came the new problems: air breathing, prevention of desiccation, support, and locomotion, and other related ones. Those plants and animals that varied in such a fashion that they were better suited to cope with any of these problems were favored, and slowly over many years and many generations, this improvement process led to a true terrestrial existence. It continued beyond the initial land plants and animals, so that the angiosperms, on the one hand, and the mammals, on the other, ultimately came into being. There is no reason to believe that these large changes are not the result of the very same mechanics of the small change of industrial melanism. One involves a small step over a few years; the other involves many many thousands of steps over millions of years.

The migration to new environments has occurred in many lesser ways also. There is, for instance, migration into the desert where the extreme problems of living differ radically for both animals and plants; and, indeed, by selection desert organisms have changed so they can cope with these extreme conditions. Migrations into high altitude have produced different fauna and flora, and certainly broad migrations into the arctic and antarctic or any other major climactic zone have had the same effect.

Another stimulus to change may be major changes in the climate of the earth that have occurred in our geological past. Consider, for instance, the ice ages when glaciers came way down over our temperate zones and then later receded. In order to exist in a particular region any group of organisms would have to make radical adaptive changes to keep abreast of the weather.

It is wrong to think that when a new organism invades a territory that is virgin and unpopulated it simply produces one adapted form. Any environment usually provides more than one opportunity, and, therefore, the new organism may diverge rapidly into a series of different forms, each of which takes advantage of a particular opportunity. This so-called adaptive radiation is a case where not just one particular type of variant is selected for but where a number of different selective forces are operating simultaneously so that the original stock will diverge in numerous directions. One of the best examples of this was discovered by Darwin himself on his voyage of the *Beagle* in the early part of the nineteenth century. He found that on the isolated Galápagos Islands there was a host of small finchlike birds that were obviously closely related. He supposed that a single species of finch happened by accident on these essentially birdless islands (at least as far as land birds were concerned) and that there were a number of different kinds of food available. Some of the finches that exist there today carry on as did their ancestors and crush seeds of various plants with their strong wedge-shaped bills. Others have become insectivorous, and their bills have become appropriately modified. Perhaps the most remarkable of all is the finch that eats grubs from trees in the manner of our woodpeckers. However, it lacks the necessary long, spiked bill, so it picks up a cactus spike and uses it as a probe in the crevices of the bark. This is often cited as an example of the use of tools by animals, an ability that is sometimes claimed to be the sole province of man. Of the dozen or so species of finch each has slightly different habits, and each makes use of different environmental niches that the Galápagos Islands have to offer. It is a convincing demonstration of the importance of the environment imposing different selection pressures on a species, and it was one of the important observations that set Darwin on his chain of reasoning that led to his theory of evolution (Figure 9).

One of the consequences of the selection pressures on the Galápagos was the production of new species, in fact, the conversion of one original species into many. From the very beginning this was recognized as an important part of the evolutionary process; Darwin even called his book *The Origin of Species by Means of Natural Selection.* A species is thought of as a group of organisms that can, within their own population, produce fertile offspring but that cannot produce viable hybrids with related forms. In other words, species is a reproductive entity. The reason this kind of reproductive isolation is considered important is that, to put the matter in the crudest terms, if all species of animals and of plants were able to successfully hybridize with one another, each evolutionary step forward would be erased by diluting the advance in hybrids. Evolution by selection tends to carve out new and unique forms while

Fig. 9 Three of Darwin's finches from the Galápagos Islands. Presumably these finches are all derived from a common ancestor. Some have retained finchlike habits and crush seeds with their large bills (right); others have become so modified as to be insectivorous or warbler-like in their habits (top); while others eat grubs in the manner of our woodpeckers (bottom).

excessive hybridization tends to make all forms the same and produce great uniformity. The only way to keep the new forms is to find ways of isolating them, so that ultimately they may lose the power of hybridization. Evolution, therefore, is not an entirely continuous process but proceeds in a series of steps, and these steps are the species.

There are a number of methods by which isolation occurs in the creating of new species. One of the most important methods and certainly the easiest to observe is that of geographic isolation. If a species becomes separated by a mountain range or a large body of water then its members can no longer crossbreed; they are physically separated. Should the separated groups then be subject to slightly different selection pressures, they will slowly diverge and become distinct. Eventually the process would reach a point where, if suddenly they were brought together again by removing the barrier, the two races could no longer crossbreed; they would become separate species. Examples of this are common, and there are many well-authenticated ones for both animals and plants. In plants, because there is no means of movement, of running or flying from one region to another, the barriers can often be smaller and still produce effective isolation and species formation.

In other cases one species may produce two, even though they inhabit the same region. This can be accomplished because any one region has many parts to it, and it can readily maintain two populations that will not intermingle. For instance, there are known instances in which species of flies or other insects will separate into two races, one that lives in the treetops and the other near the ground. They may change in other respects, such as the time of breeding activity in the day, and, therefore, even though they live close to one another, they are effectively isolated and can give rise to separate species. This is a kind of ecological isolation.

As far as the methods of preventing crossbreeding that may arise in either geographic or ecological isolation there are a whole number of mechanisms that will prevent hybridization. The simplest, found in both animals and plants, is one of timing. The different races either effect fertilization at separate times of the day (as in the case just mentioned), or the whole breeding seasons will not coincide. In most organisms there are chemical means of preventing successful mating between races and species; they may operate on any step in the long sequence of chemical events leading to successful fertilization. Sometimes fertilization is accomplished, but the resulting embryo never reaches maturity. Finally, as in the case of mules, hybrids are produced, but they are sterile and cannot propagate.

In the matter of hybridization, as will be seen when we enter the subject of genetics, plants have some special properties of their own in which they differ from animals, and one of these is that plants may actually produce new species by making viable hybrids. So here is an exception to the rule of isolation that we have been expounding, and this exception is itself used in making species.

Besides chemical methods of assuring isolation, animals have still another that is of recent interest. Courtship in animals involves a complex behavioral pattern in which the male and the female go through a series of ritual actions, each one being dependent on the previous appropriate action of the partner. If closely related races of fruit flies or fish (both of these happen to have been intensively studied) are brought together, it is discovered that, because of some slight difference in one of the steps of the ritual, the courtship will be abruptly stopped at some specific point. Therefore, slight differences in these patterns are an effective means of preventing hybridization.

Paleontologists as well as ecologists have been for some years studying the evolutionary factors we have discussed and have continuously attempted to see how the fossil record, on the one hand, or the present-day distribution of animals and plants, on the other, fit in with this scheme. There seem to be no major discrepancies, and a general feeling that the mechanism of evolution is understood prevails, particularly in regard to the importance of selection and the method of formation of new species.

If we turn to the evolution of groups above the level of species, that is, the evolution of genera, families, orders, classes, and even phyla, we come to a slightly more controversial matter. There are some who place great emphasis on the discontinuities, the gaps between the major groups and feel that these steps must have occurred by some kind of large saltations the exact nature of which is not clear. The opposite view is that the gaps represent simple disappearances of the intermediate steps. Another old problem is that certain lines of evolution seem to have a directiveness to them; they go in a straight line (as is shown particularly well in the evolution of the horse) while other lines seem to radiate in all directions. This straight line evolution or orthogenesis was ascribed to special evolutionary forces, but the modern view again is that selection in the proper ecological and geographical environment is more than sufficient to account for the phenomenon. In some cases the selection pressures are diffuse, and one has radiating patterns as with Darwin's finches. In others the selection pressure is narrow and uniform, as with the evolution of horses. In this case the selection pressure for increase of size alone accounts for much of the apparent directiveness of the evolutionary change. One of the most striking and forceful ways selection shows its power is in the phenomenon of convergence. If there is pressure for a particular function, any living organism present in that environment may respond. Insects, birds, and bats all developed wings and invaded the air; a similar selection pressure had a similar effect on three totally unrelated groups.

In the matter of radiating evolution versus evolution in a line we see that this same dual system of selection operated during the course of the evolution of the main kingdoms and phyla. The first cells seem to have radiated and tried many different experiments in multicellularity. Only some were successful in those early environments and they shot forward in straight lines to produce more complex forms. But interlaced with the forward spurts there are further periods of experimenting, further periods of radiation. Evolution goes by spurts and stops. Even the rate of change itself, which can be accurately measured in those forms that have left a fossil record, varies, and some groups such as the mollusks have been exceedingly slow in their progress while others, such as the mammals, have been very rapid. Again this can be totally understood in terms of selection in particular environments. No other hypothetical mechanisms seem to be necessary to account for the facts as we know them.

CHAPTER 3

GENETICS

Genetics is the study of controlled variation and its transmission from one generation to the next. It is not sufficient for one organism to differ from another to have it be of any use in selection and evolution. The difference must be inherited. For instance, if we paint a moth black near an industrial center, this might possibly improve the chances of survival of the particular moth; but it certainly would in no way help his offspring.

One of the simplest methods of heritable variation, which is conveniently illustrated among bacteria and other single-celled organisms, is mutation. Mutation is a change in the chemical structure of a gene, and all the progeny of this mutant cell will have the mutant character. This method by itself is useful to bacteria, because the cell generations are rapid, and the number of cells in any one population are generally large. If the cells are put in a new environment, it is conceivable that one of the mutants will have a selective advantage over all the other cells; in this way, by a sort of hit and miss, trial and error, the new environment can be invaded.

There is a well-known example of this phenomenon. If bacterial cells are placed in a culture dish with penicillin, the majority of the many millions of cells will cease their growth; but occasionally one cell will mutate to a penicillin-resistant form, and a small colony will begin to grow in the dish. Here is an adverse environment in which all the cells are inhibited in their growth; yet by a sudden change in a gene that in turn changes some of the cell machinery, one cell can grow and invade. This, of course, is exactly what has happened in the bacterial populations that are pathogenic to man, and for this reason it is urged that antibiotics be used only when necessary so as to decrease the chances of making all human pathogens antibiotic resistant.

It is easy in the laboratory to perform other kinds of selection experiments. In some cases just one mutant takes over, and the parent type disappears, as is true in the example given above. In others the mutant will remain in the population along with the parent type, and the two cell types maintain as they grow a constant ratio in their numbers. The reason for this has been analyzed, and it is known that the two cell types produce substances that limit the growth and, therefore, the cell number of the other. By this chemical means a population balance is reached, and this example serves as a model for cell interactions or interactions between individuals —a topic to which we will return.

In the experiment with penicillin there will, of course, be other mutations besides this particular one, and the other ones will likely be of no value in this environment. Roughly, under normal circumstances, one cell in every 200,000 will have a chance of some sort of mutation. As yet there is no known way to direct a mutation in a specific direction, although various chemical agents and particularly radiation—for example, X-rays or ultraviolet light—will cause an over-all increase in the mutation rate. Mutation, it is presumed, involves a change in the structure of the DNA molecules (desoxyribonucleic acids), and the effect of this change is transferred to the cytoplasm. DNA is a complex molecule with a specific structure, and by duplication it can make molecules identical to itself that are passed on to the daughter cells in growth and cell division.

An especially interesting discovery was made a few years ago, and that is if extracts of the DNA from one type of bacteria were added to the cells of another, the cells of the second strain would take on the character of the first. In other words the added DNA influences the DNA production of the dividing intact cells so that a true and permanent genetic change has occurred. At first it might be argued that this is an example of directed mutation, but this would not provide a helpful description of the events. The added

DNA somehow manages to get into a position where it can be responsible for the new synthesis of DNA. The process is called transformation, and in contrast to mutation, which might be compared to an error in a code, transformation is as though a whole new code sheet were slipped into the works.

It can be seen at a glance that the system of variation by simple mutation of bacteria has many limitations that make it inefficient. The main point is that there is no reserve; all the genetic cards of each cell are held out in the open. There is no capacity, except by chance mutation, to carry traits that could be responsible for variation in future generations. Coupled with this is the fact that, since all the cells have the same genetic constitution, there is no opportunity for shuffling the traits.

The most rudimentary kind of shuffling occurs in some primitive multicellular organisms. In the cellular slime molds the individual amoebae feed first and then later aggregate into masses that ultimately form small fruiting bodies. If a colony is started from one cell, then unless mutation has occurred the cell mass will be genetically homogeneous. But it has been shown that the cells that aggregate are sometimes of a difficult genetic constitution, so that if one thinks of the genetics of whole cell masses, they may have a variety of genes depending upon the cells that entered into it. This means that any one slime mold could have more than two parents. Its particular character and its success in selection will depend upon its conglomerate genetic constitution. At sporulation each spore consists of a single amoeba, and, therefore, when these spores are disseminated there are all sorts of new possible combinations for the next generation of aggregated masses. Admittedly there is some hazard in the system, for in each generation the proper combination of cell types may not necessarily come together; but the great advantage of the system is that by carrying cells of diverse types as reserves, the whole mass is more likely to have a hardy cell type that can immediately adapt to a new adverse environment. It does not have to rely solely, as did the bacteria in our previous example, upon the chance possibility of an appropriate mutation. This new insurance method of the cellular molds means also that a large number of short generations are no longer necessary to insure that new and perhaps adverse environments will be satisfactorily conquered.

There are a number of other ways of keeping an extra hoard of diverse traits or genes and reshuffling them in different ways in the offspring to produce variation in the individual progeny, but by far the most common and the most successful is that of sexuality. Sex is the keystone to variation production; it is a beautifully efficient method of handling and transmitting variation. It is found in all the groups of animals and plants from the lowest to the highest. In fact wherever there are cells one finds sexuality, for the mechanics of the sexual process are bound to the structure of the cells. One of the more surprising recent discoveries is that of J. Lederberg and E. L. Tatum, who found that some bacteria also have a sexual system. In this case it is not yet possible to see all the mechanical details, although there are indications that, at least, there must be functional similarities between the gene systems and the chromosomes of bacteria and those of higher cellular forms.

In most higher sexual forms the adults possess a double set of chromosomes (*i.e.*, they are diploid), that is, each chromosome has its twin alongside it. The twin chromosomes may not be identical in that at homologous points on the chromosomes one gene may be a mutant form of the other. If the gene pairs differ, then they are called heterozygous for this character; and if they are the same, they are homozygous for this character. The advantage of having two sets of chromosomes is that in heterozygous individuals (and in nature individuals usually are fairly heterozygous) it is possible to keep a file of extra genes that can contribute to making variable offspring.

The gametes, the sperm and the egg, of these individuals are haploid, that is, they have only one set of chromosomes. This means that somewhere in the formation of the gametes there must have been a special cell division that resulted in the twin pairs of chromosomes separating from one another. This special division actually occurs in two steps and is called meiosis.

Meiosis is no more than a specialized mitosis. In mitosis, which accompanies cell division, there is a duplication of each chromosome so that all the traits (genes) of the mother cell can be present in both of the daughter cells. It is a perfectly devised system whereby exact duplication can be effected with the minimum number of parts necessary; if the genes were just randomly distributed throughout the cells, there would have to be many more than two of each to be certain that each daughter cell possessed a full complement of genes after cleavage. In one of the two meiotic divisions there is no chromosome duplication, so that instead of a new pair of chromosomes going to each cell, as in mitosis, only one member of the pair goes, giving a haploid sperm or egg. If one remembers now that the two chromosomes in a pair can be heterozygous, that is, possess different genes at equivalent points or loci, then the gametes produced will be different in their gene content. Not only that, but suppose a heterozygous organism contained in the diploid state four pairs of chromosomes, Aa, Bb, Cc, and Dd. By separating these in meiosis there are a whole number of different possible gametes: ABCD, Abcd, ABcd, ABCd, etc. So variability is assured by this system, and the greater the number of chromosomes, the greater the possible number of different gametes (Figure 10).

The argument thus far has been purely cytological on what can be deduced from chromosome behavior, and it will be helpful to pause here and show that this information ties in perfectly with that of the great discoveries of biology. In 1866 Mendel published a paper on the inheritance of peas in which he crossed plants with purple and white flowers. The first generation gave flowers that were all purple, and when these were crossed with each other, the second generation gave a mixture of white and purple flowers. By counting the number of these progeny he showed that one quarter of the flowers were white and three quarters were purple. From these facts Mendel made the following remarkable deductions: that the characters were inherited as units and that one character could be dominant over the other, in this case purple being dominant over white (Figure 11).

In a purebred purple pea all the characters will be dominant purple (PP), and in the white they will be recessive white (pp). Therefore, in the first cross the offspring will have both a dominant purple and a recessive white (Pp); but since purple is dominant, the actual color of the plant will be purple. These first-generation

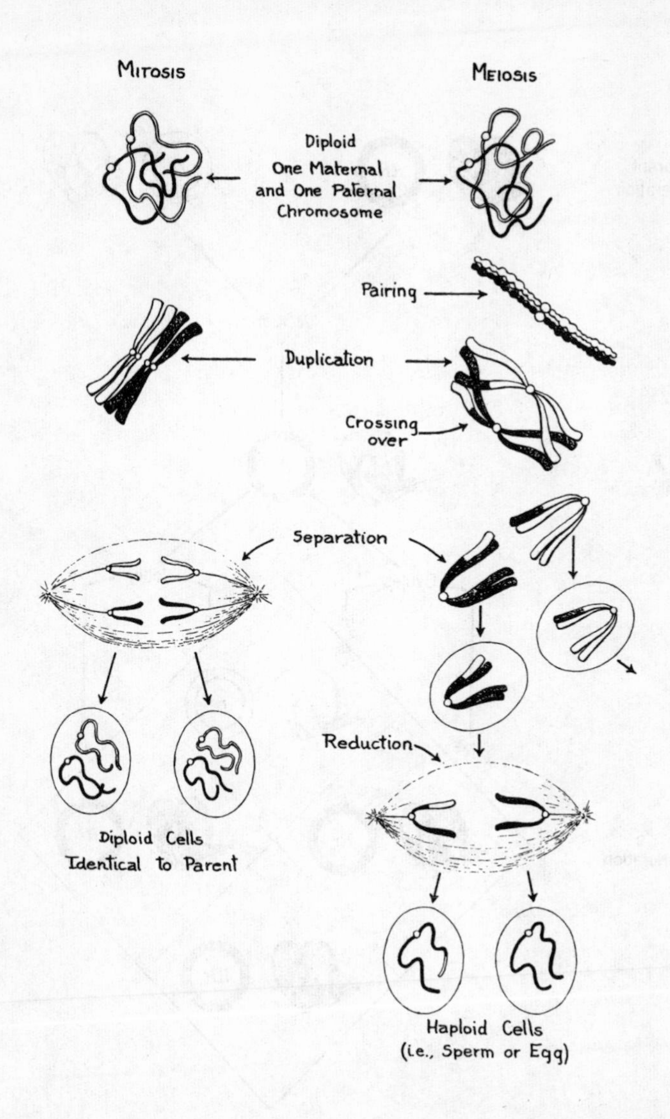

Fig. 10 A comparison of mitosis and meiosis. Note that in mitosis the end result is identical to the parent cell, while in the two divisions of meiosis the number of chromosomes has been reduced by half and parts of the chromosomes have been exchanged in the process of crossing over.

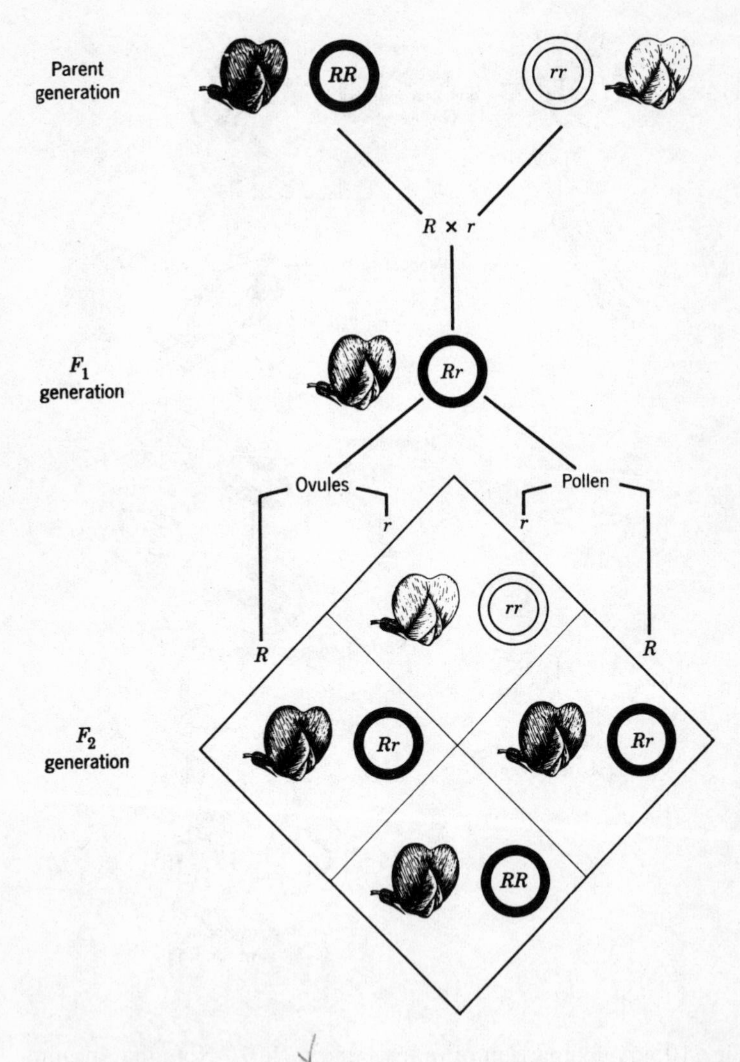

Fig. 11 Mendel's first law, or the law of segregation. R is for the gene purple and r for white flower color. Black rings and white rings symbolize purple and white flowers respectively. (From C. B. Anfinsen after T. Dobzhansky.)

purple plants will now produce two kinds of pollen or ovules: those containing the dominant purple character (P) and those with the recessive white (p). These give four possible combinations, of which the following three will show purple flowers: PP, Pp, and pP; and the fourth pp will be white, giving the 3:1 ratio discovered in the actual experiment.

If we now substitute the notion of paired chromosomes and have a homozygous, dominant purple pea crossed with a homozygous, recessive white pea, then we can clearly see that this experiment of Mendel's is understood completely in terms of the chromosome behavior that we have just described. This is even more evident in a second experiment of Mendel's where two chromosomes are involved. In fact this experiment gave rise to Mendel's law of independent assortment, and the reason the assortment is independent is that the two pairs of characters tested are on different pairs of chromosomes; and as we have just seen, the chromosomes do assort independently into the gametes, and one can get a variety of different combinations (Figure 12).

Again using peas, Mendel bred pure strains having yellow, smooth seeds with those having green, wrinkled seeds. Because of the principle of dominance, the first generation all appeared yellow and smooth; but when they were crossbred they gave four types of offspring in the following ratios; nine yellow, smooth; three yellow, wrinkled; three green, smooth; and one green, wrinkled. If this is analyzed either in terms of characters, as Mendel did, or in terms of two pairs of genes on two pairs of chromosomes, we can see that the homozygous parent, yellow, smooth pea had character YY on one pair of chromosomes and SS on the other, while the homozygous, green, wrinkled pea was recessive and possessed yy and ss. This gave the following constitution to the first generation: Yy on one chromosome and Ss on the other. Since these pairs of chromosomes could assort independently, there were the possible gametes: YS, yS, Ys, and ys. By the crossing of all these for gamete types, the final 9:3:3:1 ratio was obtained.

Not only was this brilliant and fundamental work of Mendel not known to the world for some years after its publication but the study of cell structure was in a most rudimentary state at the time,

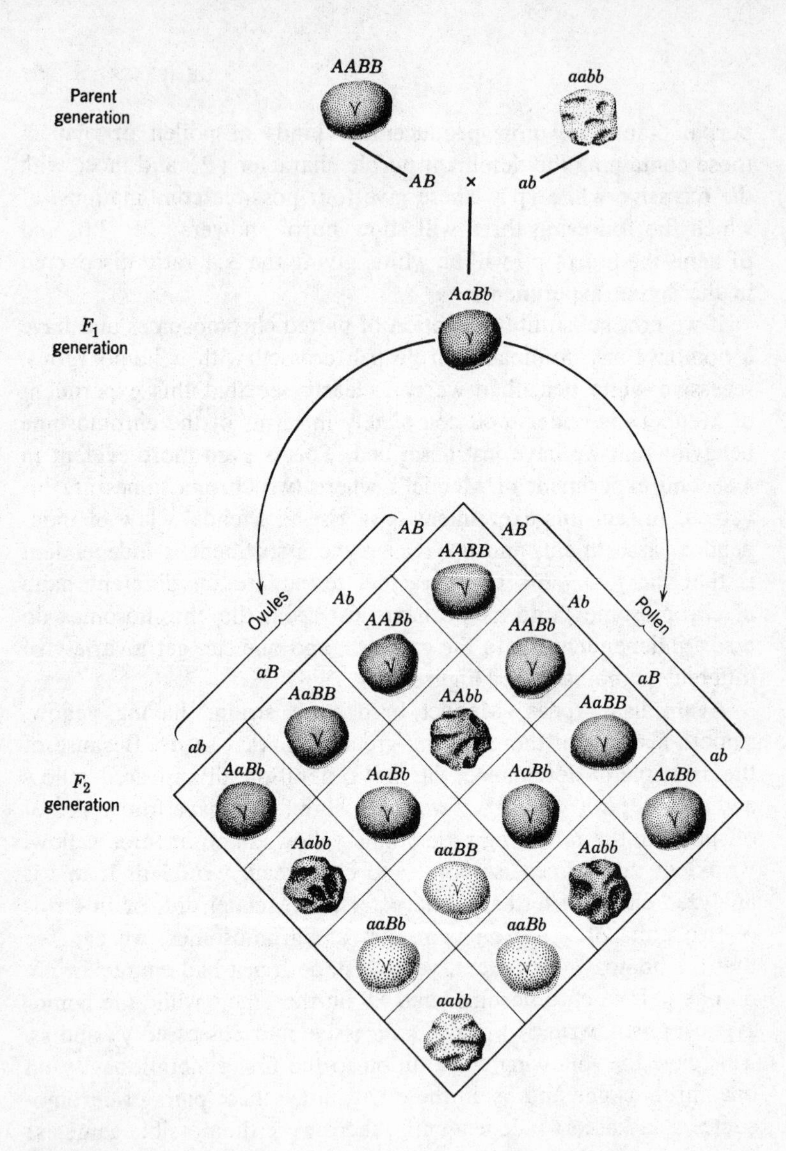

Fig. 12 Mendel's second law, or the law of independent assortment. A and a indicate the genes for yellow and green colors, respectively, and B and b indicate those for smooth and wrinkled seeds. Yellow is dominant over green and smooth is dominant over wrinkled. (From C. B. Anfinsen, after T. Dobzhansky.)

and Mendel himself had no picture of how these characters were contained within the cell. It was not until the early part of this century, well after the laws of heredity had been discovered, along with the details of meiosis, that it was realized that together the two lines of investigation made perfect sense; the one was the physical basis of the other. This led to a flurry of activity in the study of genetics, and great strides were soon made, especially by T. H. Morgan and his co-workers on the fruit fly *Drosophila*.

The next step forward was the realization that the sexual system was even cleverer at character-shuffling or gene-recombination than had been supposed. On the genetic side a whole number of mutant characters were obtained, and by breeding experiments it could be shown that the characters either assorted independently or not; if they did not, they were on the same chromosome. Since *Drosophila* has only four chromosomes, it was possible to group all the characters into four groups. But periodically two pairs of genes that were known to be on the same pair of chromosomes, apparently violating all that has been said thus far, sorted out independently. The hypothesis suggested to account for this sudden switch is that the chromosomes somehow split—both members of the pair at the same point—and the broken ends hooked up again with a new partner. This so-called crossing over involves the mutual exchange of whole segments of the chromosome. On the structural level it was known that during the first division of meiosis there is a winding together of the chromosome pairs so that they touch at homologous points. It is even possible to see cross connections at places where they seem almost bound together. It is now known that during this pairing process, the crossing over, the exchange of parts takes place so that during the second meiotic division, when the pairs of chromosomes are separated, the new chromosomes may be a mosaic made up of parts of both of the original diploid chromosomes (Figure 10).

This is, indeed, a kind of supershuffling, for there are both the recombination of the whole chromosomes and then the possible recombination of parts of the chromosome. Coupled with this is the constant possibility that any of the genes may become altered by mutation. In other words the system of change that we saw in nonsexual bacteria is superimposed upon the chromosome-shuffling as a further source of variation.

Somehow, when the process is put in this fashion, one is left with the impression that mutation is rather secondary; but it is really the factor of fundamental importance. Since mutation means a chemical change in the gene structure, all progressive advancements must ultimately be by mutation, and all that can be done by recombination is to shuffle what is given by mutation. Gene mutation provides the raw material for evolution, and recombination sets this material out in different ways so that selection may be furthered by being provided with a whole series of possible arrangements.

The word mutation is used to mean any sudden appearance of a new character (as opposed to the unmasking of a recessive character already present). This naturally includes the kind of mutation we have been discussing where a gene becomes altered in some way. But there is another way new traits can be caused to appear, and this is by chromosome rearrangements. What happens is that sometimes during the first division of meiosis errors are made, and extra bits of chromosome may be added, or a segment of a chromosome may be inverted. These new chromosome arrangements will themselves result in new traits. We can then add one more method in which the sexual system can produce variation.

There is one further and somewhat related system that is found solely in plants. This is the doubling, quadrupling, or even further increasing of the whole set of chromosomes. Such polyploidy, as it is called, produces new characters, new traits that are often advantageous in a particular environment. Many of our common plants have polyploid varieties. It is not certain why this is so rare in animals, although it is suspected that it is because of the fact that it produces an imbalance in the sex chromosomes—the chromosomes that determine maleness and femaleness—and this results in immediate sterility of the offspring of animals.

When all the diverse ways in which sexuality can produce variation are considered, it is not surprising that so efficient a system, involving only single cells (for meiosis and fertilization are cellular processes), is found everywhere in the plant and animal kingdoms. That it has been useful in evolution is demonstrated by the fact that it has been retained in evolution. Selection reaches with its delicate fingers into every recess of the living organisms, and the sexual system is one of its finest achievements—so fine that it has been kept in perfect working order, with no modern improvements necessary, since the first formation of cellular organisms, if not before.

The rather breezy implication given so far in this discussion of genetics is that all is known, and to set the record straight it may be useful to examine a few points of special interest in current biological research. The principal one is the nature of the gene, and along with this lies the problem of the nature of mutation.

One of the first experiments to give some information about the gene was that of Morgan and his co-workers in which they were able to determine the approximate position of the gene and the exact order of the genes on the chromosome. The method made use of crossing over, with the simple assumption that the amount of crossing over between two characters was proportionate to the distance between their genes on the chromosomes. The amount of crossing over was determined by making a cross involving two characters that are known to be on the same chromosome, that is, that ordinarily do not sort out independently but stay together. Since crossing over involves a break in the chromosome, if two genes are far apart, the greater distance on one chromosome between them offers a greater chance that a break might occur in the region. In this way it was possible to make gene maps for each of the four chromosomes of *Drosophila* and to indicate the distance between the genes in crossover units.

While this work was being carried out, a large bit of good luck turned up. It was shown that the salivary glands of the developing fruit-fly larvae had peculiar, swollen, giant nuclei, with giant chromosomes (Figure 15). If these were spread out and suitably stained, one saw a series of bands. The next step, which used some clever detective work (involving among other things flies with aberrations on their chromosomes that are correlated with specific character peculiarities), was to identify specific bands with specific genes and to make the gene maps far more immediate and real. It was known that the bands of the giant salivary chromosomes were caused by the duplication of the strands of the normal chromosome as the gland cells became enlarged. Therefore, it was presumed that in a single strand one would have a series of swellings, each of which would be a gene. This led to the simplified notion (that geneticists have been trying to stamp out of textbooks ever since) that the genes are like beads on a string, for we have seen that they lie in a linear order and that they can be identified with discrete bumps.

Soon it was realized from genetic studies that undoubtedly there must be more genes than visible bumps, but at least, the idea that the gene was an indivisible unit (a unit of recombination) remained fixed for a considerable time. Difficulties arose when it was suddenly discovered that some genes were actually groups of genes very close to one another and that crossing over could split them in various ways. Therefore, while there still is the view that there is a minimum recombination unit that is finally incapable of further splitting, there is much doubt as to how small this unit is and of what it consists. Nevertheless, the subject is being profitably pursued by geneticists, and one of the most important studies is that of S. Benzer on the splitting up of recombination units in certain viruses that have many of the genetic properties of higher organisms. Here the smallest unit incapable of further splitting is minute —perhaps comparable to one side chain of the DNA molecule— although this proposal is highly speculative.

Another approach to the nature of the genes has been by the study of mutation, especially by the use of agents, such as radiation and particular chemicals that specifically cause mutation. These methods have been coupled with the chemical evidence that the genic material is most likely composed of DNA, a substance that exhibits an unusual chemical stability. It has been shown, for instance, that the other chemicals, such as proteins and carbohydrates, are constantly resynthesized and replaced within a cell, while the DNA remains relatively unchanged. This stability is presumed to be vital to the genetic function of DNA, for only by remaining constant could it fully retain the genetic information. If it does become altered, if there is some chemical change, then this is thought to be a mutation. The DNA is stable up to a point but not so much so that no change is possible at all. X-ray and other radiations send out fast-moving particles that shoot into the cell like bullets, and if they hit a part of the DNA molecule, there is no reason to think they could not cause a structural change in the molecule. Chemical mutagens could also harass the DNA molecules in some way to cause changes. Spontaneous mutation might be thought of as some sort of error, perhaps an error made when the molecule is duplicated. But in the final analysis this examination of mutation does not give us any complete answer as to what is a gene. It tells us that, besides the fact that genic material can be subdivided by splitting, giving recombination units, it can also be altered in spots. These spots might be called units of mutation, and the units of mutation could be small, as are the units of recombination.

But what we really want to know is whether or not there is any unit for the production of specific characters, and in answer to this we can only make guesses. If DNA is the genetic substance, we know that its molecules are very large—so large it seems doubtful that one DNA molecule equals one character-forming gene. Perhaps the chromosome is made up of a continuous molecule or a continuous mass of molecules, and perhaps the gene effects are produced by certain regions of this molecular mass being responsible for the synthesis of specific substances. This idea is consistent with many of the facts that are known today, but, nevertheless, it is so highly speculative that it must be thought of with great caution. In any event the notion of genes being beads on a string, despite the simple and pleasant picture it evokes, undoubtedly must be discarded.

Before leaving the subject of the nature of the gene, there is one other aspect that is of great interest and importance. It is the fact that the order or the position of the genes upon the chromosomes has effects upon the characters produced. This dovetails with what we have just suggested, namely that the chromosome is a continuous matrix of genic material, for its over-all structure is as important as the structure of its smallest parts. One of the first demonstrations of this came from different types of chromosome aberrations. For instance, if during crossing over there is an error, and a segment of a chromosome is put back into place in reverse order, all the genes will be there, but their sequence will be reversed. This will produce definite morphological changes, such as variegated or speckled eyes in the fruit fly *Drosophila,* in the resulting adult. Another example may be seen in genes that are very close to one another. If there are two mutant genes, they will only have the effect of producing a mutant individual if there is one on each of the homologous chromosomes; if they both are on the same chromosome (and the opposite chromosome has none), the result will be a normal individual showing none of the mutant character. This again emphasizes the idea that the over-all structure of the chromosomes, that is, the specific placement of the parts, is as important as the parts themselves.

There is another slightly different bit of evidence that has a similar kind of conclusion. Not all genes have simple effects, like producing yellow and green seeds; in fact some are known to affect the action of other genes either by enhancing or reducing their effect. Genes, therefore, do not necessarily work as single units but work in concert, with some modifying the effect of others. Also there is evidence for genes that can affect the rate of spontaneous mutation and the extent of crossing over; in other words genes that will affect the amount of variation. Genes, in turn, may have not one effect but many, often on different parts of the organism. The genetic make-up or code of an organism is an interconnected complex of directions and not a simple list of unrelated items.

It will be appropriate at this juncture to take the information about genetics which has been reviewed here and see how it fits in with what we know of evolution. It would be fair to say that the greatest progress in the last twenty years in the study of evolution has been the application of the principles of genetics, and the science of genetics has also greatly benefited from this merger of the two fields. As has already been pointed out, this was the big gap in Darwin's information, and now that gap can be closed.

Let us begin with a fact just mentioned, that genes can affect the amount of variation. Great emphasis has been placed here on the idea that sexuality and its attendant genetic recombination is maintained by selection because it is such an efficient system of making highly variable offspring. This, of course, is true, but it is easy to see that there are some dangers to too much variation; the extreme would be as bad as no variation at all. It would mean that every time a variant that was successful in selection was produced it would be lost by further excessive mutation and recombination. There must be a balance, so that there are new possibilities for selection; but once these possibilities are attained they must not be eliminated. Therefore, the degree of mutation and recombination must itself be under genetic control, so that it also can be brought to the most efficient level by selection.

Not all organisms living under different conditions will want the same amount of variation, for this will be determined by a number of factors. For instance, if an organism lives in a constant environment, such as the tropics, then its offspring will face similar climatic problems the year around. Animals and plants in temperate zones will have drastic seasonal changes. This is a somewhat oversimplified case, but, nevertheless, the organisms in the tropics might find excess variation in climatic adaptation a waste, if not a danger, while those in the temperate zones would need it to meet changing conditions. Perhaps a better way to make the point is to say that when an environment is constant, and if the plant or animal is well adapted, then it may do well to stop gambling and hang on to its gains by reducing its variability. If, on the other hand, an organism is to survive some cataclysm, it can do so more effectively if it is producing highly variable offspring.

If one looks at the matter from the point of view of the evolutionary past, then any period of experimenting in which one sees many offshoots into different environmental niches is a period where the greater the variability, the more rapid the adaptive radiation. This would certainly be the case for the original finches that arrived on the Galápagos Islands. In contrast, if one has a straight line evolution where there is a simple, forward progression, as in the evolution of the horse, then one would expect a lower degree of variability.

We turn now to the way in which the variability is controlled. We have already seen that there is a direct gene control over the amount of mutation and the amount of recombination. Since genes can be selected for or against, this is an easy way to select for the degree of variation. For the most part, regulation of the mutation rate and chromosome recombination must be the methods employed, although now and then we see a far more radical method. It is radical because it fixes the organism, and since it is irreversible, it probably prevents all future change. It is merely that if an organism finds a particularly suitable environment for which it appears to be adapted, then it can cease all sexual reproduction and reproduce asexually. In other words, once led to its Garden of Eden, it will settle down for good and sever its sole method of any future progress. It will be constant and stable as long as the Garden of Eden exists, but it will be ill-prepared to meet, for instance, the advent of an ice age. There are various ways in which the sexual reproduction is stopped and the asexual maintained. In many lower plants and even in higher ones there are separate means of asexual reproduction, so, once sexuality goes, these take over permanently. For instance, in the case of buffalo grass, which covers much of our Western plains and is certainly successful and well adapted, the plant multiplies by vegetative propagation, by sending out roots that sprout new shoots. In animals that lack any means of asexual reproduction there is reproduction by parthenogenesis. That is, the egg will develop, without the addition of the sperm, so that the sexual machine is employed but without the sex and without the fertilization and recombination. A number of insects, including aphids or plant lice, do this.

There is also an interesting intermediate situation in which an organism will reproduce parthenogenetically or asexually during the summer months when conditions are constant; but at the end of the fall they will have a final phase of reproduction that will be sexual. The fertilized egg will usually form a resistant body that lasts through the winter months, and, come spring, when new opportunities lie ahead, the variable recombined offspring will germinate and grow; and some of them will perhaps be adapted to the new environments.

Another less extreme method of reducing variation, other than the reproduction becoming asexual, is for inbreeding to be permitted. Inbreeding, as seen, for instance, in brother-sister matings, tends to reduce the variability; with successive generations of such inbreeding, the genes of all the individuals may be identical (homozygous), and this is a truly purebred line. Many plants and some animals are hermaphroditic, that is, they bear both the male and female sex organs; if they fertilize themselves, they have only one parent, and they will achieve complete genetic uniformity, complete homozygosity even more rapidly.

Perhaps of greater interest is the opposite situation in which there is an elaborate mechanism to preserve crossbreeding and, therefore, to maintain a reasonable degree of variability. The disadvantage of inbreeding is that bad recessive genes may be unmasked and, therefore, may produce abnormal offspring. Of course, the opposite is equally likely to be true, and favorable recessive genes may lead to exceptionally good offspring. Race horses are inbred by animal husbandry men to try to preserve the good recessive genes and eliminate the bad.

Plants have by far the most elaborate means of insuring crossbreeding. The reason for this is partly that a great many plants are hermaphroditic and must insure against self-fertilization, and even those that have separate male and female individuals are nonmotile and, therefore, are at the mercy of the wind or insects for cross-pollination. If crossbreeding is selectively advantageous, the problem of preventing brother-sister mating is not inconsiderable. There are a variety of mechanisms, of which the simplest is a matter of timing. If on any one hermaphroditic plant the pollen and the ovule mature at separate times, then they are never able to fertilize themselves. The other methods are chemical, and for one reason or another there is an incompatability between the pollen of a plant and its own tissue around the ovary so that its pollen simply cannot penetrate into its ovary. This has been carefully studied in a number of cases and the general nature of the chemical reactions identified, and furthermore, the genes that control the chemical blocking have been identified; we know a considerable amount about the genetics of the prevention of self-fertilization.

Animals do not seem to have these elaborate systems of chemical incompatability except for a few groups, such as the ascidians (sea squirts or tunicates), where like plants there are hermaphroditic adults incapable of locomotion. It would seem that if organisms can move and if there are male and female individuals, the chance that brothers and sisters will mate is automatically reduced. In some animals there may be patterns of behavior, such as the normal separation or scattering of litter mates before sexual maturity, but mostly there is no evident mechanism but just a scrambling of the distribution of individuals by locomotion. This means that there still will be some inbreeding, but its amount will be negligible.

A parenthetical note should be made here concerning man. We have no genetic-chemical system of preventing brother-sister matings nor any deep-seated psychological or instinctive reasons (so far as we can tell), except those that are induced by a very strong social taboo. Aside from a few royal dynasties, such as the Ptolemies, all human societies from the more primitive to the more advanced have an incest taboo. But this is an entirely different matter from a genetic method of ensuring cross-fertilization, and in a later chapter we will have time to examine more carefully the differences between genetic and cultural inheritance. The interesting thing here is that even though the incest taboo is produced by an entirely different mechanism, it serves the same function of preventing inbreeding, maintaining a large number of extra genes by keeping the individuals heterozygous and in this way keeping the population variable so that natural selection may occur.

In the course we have pursued thus far it has been shown that variation, without which evolution cannot take place, can be understood in terms of genes and their behavior within the chromosomes of cells. Besides an attempt to see what little we know of the nature of these genes, we have also examined the sexual system and various ramifications of it to see how the variation is handled as well as transmitted. This brings us to the last phase of our discussion of the relation of genetics to evolution in which we must not think of evolutionary mechanisms in terms of structural or functional changes as we did in the previous chapter but must think of them in terms of gene changes within the population.

These studies are primarily mathematical and have stemmed from the brilliant imaginations of J. B. S. Haldane, R. A. Fisher, and Sewall Wright. No attempt will be made here to see even the beginning of the mathematical framework, but it will be possible to give an easy word-picture of the method of some of the results of the so-called population genetics.

First one must make the assumption that in a population there is unrestricted crossbreeding. One would not expect from what we have just said of crossbreeding that all the individuals in the populations would have the same genes; quite to the contrary, one would expect a large variety of different genetic constitutions. However, instead of considering the genes of any one individual, one could consider the total number of different kinds of genes in the whole population and their frequency of occurrence. This mass of genes in a population is the gene pool. If the population is to undergo evolutionary change, this can be translated to mean that there has been a shift in the constitution of the gene pool.

What are the factors that affect this gene pool? The most obvious is the rate of mutation, and each gene can be given a definite value as to its likelihood of appearing in the population. Another obvious factor is the selection pressure for a particular gene. If the gene is advantageous in a special environment, it will be favored, and the degree to which it is favored can be given a definite value. Negative selection, that is, elimination of genes, can be treated in the same way. The population size is another factor of great importance, and it in turn will affect the consequences of mutation and selection in the rate of spread of any particular gene.

To give some examples: if a population is small and the mutation rate high, a new gene can invade the population in a short time, while in a large population the time required is much greater. As far as selection is concerned, if the population is large, selection makes changes in the frequency of a gene at a slow rate, while the change is faster in a small population. Often the matter is further complicated by the fact that there are fluctuations in the population sizes; and in extreme cases, such as the lemmings of the North, there will be a definite periodicity of the fluctuations. Therefore, the effectiveness of selection and mutation as agents of change will in turn fluctuate.

Another factor that affects the gene pool is the movements of the organisms. In animals this is readily achieved, for they can wander freely with their well-developed system of locomotion; but in plants that are rooted to the ground movement from one region to another is a more subtle matter. Some plants can wander by having their seed carried in the water (*e.g.,* coconuts) or by the wind (*e.g.,* dandelion) or by animals eating the seeds and depositing them intact in some remote spot (after their passage through the alimentary tract). And as far as pollination is concerned, wind and insects and even birds will sometimes cross-pollinate plants that are great distances apart. All of this will favor the movements of genes from one part of a population to another or even from one population to another.

It has been possible both in the laboratory and to some extent in nature to test the predicted mathematical consequences of the interactions of all these factors, and so far the agreement has been good. One of the methods employed in the laboratory is the use of population boxes. Some fruit flies with known genetic constitution are placed in the box and kept there for long periods of time. All that is done to them is to provide new food every few days so they can produce young and have a series of generations. The environment is constant and the crossbreeding indiscriminate, and, therefore, the effect of selection in this particular environment can be carefully followed. If new mutants appear, they can be detected and their success ascertained. The experimental verification of the mathematical generalizations about genetic change in a population may not seem like very much of an advance in our knowledge, but it does serve to show that our understanding of the genetic basis of evolution is sound and real.

If this is the case, there is one problem that has been troubling to many in the past and should be briefly considered here. This is that the large majority of the mutants that appear in the laboratory or in nature are so very small in their effects it is thought they cannot account for the large changes we observe in the over-all evolution of animals and plants. In the fruit fly we have mutants that affect eye color, bristle number, wing shape, etc., all of which are negligible changes. Related to this problem is the difficulty that the majority of the mutants appear to be backward steps rather than forward ones. They often involve the loss of some structure, and along with this it must be remembered that the most frequent kinds of mutation by far are "lethals," that is, they result in the early death of the developing offspring.

There can be no real black-or-white, proof-or-disproof answer to these difficulties but only a reasonable argument to show why they are likely not to be difficulties at all. In the first place one would expect change to be by small increments, and if one has enough of these over millions of years, the final changes can be very large indeed. If changes had to take large steps, the chance that these large steps would produce some unbalance in the offspring that would result in their death would be great. The inner machinery of the organism is so delicately balanced that viable changes must be small. That so many mutations are lethal would substantiate this point, for they probably are major mutations; but at the same time, they upset an internal balance and cannot be sustained. Some biologists have argued that the major gaps between phyla or even classes were caused by extra-large mutation jumps. It supposes that once in a great while a particular large mutation was viable and did persist. Again there is no way of eliminating this hypothesis, and the only counter argument that can effectively be put forth is that it is unnecessary to make such an assumption. The small mutational increments could well have spanned the gap between groups, and the few fossil intermediates have failed to be discovered. Perhaps it is not important to decide whether these "mega-" mutations have occurred or not, but it does seem important not to forget the hypothesis that evolution as it has occurred on the earth could have occurred without them.

On the question of the majority of mutations being regressive rather than progressive, Haldane makes the point that many mutations are back mutations; that is, the mutant type reverts back to the original wild type, and if this is so, then one of these two steps (the original mutation and its reversion to normal) must have been a leap forward. Of course, one still might argue that this forward step only brings one back to the starting line; but then one can turn to other examples. In laboratory tests in population boxes and in nature new mutations have appeared that are progressive in the sense that they are needed and selected for. The melanistic moths in the industrial areas of Britain and other parts of Europe are perfect examples. Another would be the mutation that permits bacteria to grow in the presence of penicillin. We could list many others. But the sceptic would again say that these are paltry changes —what about changes that led to something as significant as the eye of a mammal? This example is always given, because it is argued that the improvements must have been made before any image formation could have been achieved, before the early eye beginnings could have had a selective advantage and that they must have developed in some mysterious way so that ultimately they led to the completed goal, the functional eye. The possibility that this is nonsense is pretty good, because if we look at primitive light receptor organs, which amount to primitive eyes, existing in some present-day invertebrates, we see they are adaptive even though they are simple; they clearly must be maintained by selection. Therefore the notion that mammalian eyes went through an inadaptive period in preparation for a future goal and were kept intact by some mysterious force seems an unnecessary and certainly unhelpful hypothesis. All the facts of the case can be interpreted by the hypothesis that we are suggesting here: a series of small gene-controlled or mutant steps where each step is adaptive and controlled by natural selection. This view requires on our part a special kind of patience for past events; it lacks mystery and is not complicated, but, nevertheless, it is a most reasonable hypothesis and will be kept until we find a better one.

CHAPTER 4

DEVELOPMENT

Neither a discussion of evolution nor a discussion of genetics can be complete without a discussion of development. The three are intimately bound together; each is really part of the other. Evolution is achieved by the selection of genes that are presented in changing arrays each generation primarily through the operation of sexuality; and development is the period in the life history of an individual when the genes act, when they convey their instructions to the individual. Therefore, if a gene is responsible for the character of short wings in the fruit fly or some extra bristles, then the instructions for these changes are passed on to the organism during the period of development. Development is synonymous with gene action.

It might well seem troublesome, at first glance, that each generation a large animal such as a human being or a big tree would start off as a minute egg and bother to go through all the tremendous changes of development, slowly progressing to the adult individual. Is not all this transformation each generation more trouble than it is worth? Would it not be easier for the adult to somehow cleave in two; then all that would be needed would be a bit of growth to restore the original size? We already have the key to why this cannot be.

This is, of course, just what does happen in single celled organisms. In *Euglena,* for instance, there is a mitosis and a cell cleavage, and then each daughter cell simply restores its size by feeding and taking in energy. But, as we have seen, during the course of evolution there has been a selection pressure for the increase in size of individuals, that is, the production of multicellular organisms. At the same time we have stressed that one of the prime conditions for evolutionary progress of any sort is sexuality. Furthermore, the sexual system, with its meiosis and fertilization, is a single-celled process. It involves one nucleus, each containing the haploid number of chromosomes, from each parent, and these fuse to form the diploid nucleus that is the beginning of the next generation. Sexuality with all its chromosome recombination, which is so vital to the production of variation, cannot operate in any other way.

Therefore, selection apparently is simultaneously working in two directions at once: it favors both large individuals and single cells that are required by sexuality. The only solution is that one stage of the life history must be small and the other large, and between these two we have a development. Development is, therefore, the inevitable result of sex and size. Even when sexual reproduction is for some reason absent, asexual reproduction has a small stage. Often this is an advantage in dispersal, and many asexual spores are minute and readily transported by the wind or passing insects. In other words it may be better to make the more general statement that development is the inevitable result of reproduction and size.

The implication from this is that development is restricted to the phase between fertilization and maximum size. This is the conventional definition of development, but it is quite a different matter from calling (as we have just done) development the period of gene action. We could bring the two together by saying that development is the period of most active gene action, but I am not sure that in so doing we will not obscure an important point. The cessation of growth may not be such a significant landmark, for there are important changes after, as well as before, this milestone. And, furthermore, the stoppage may not be one abrupt moment but may occur at different times in different parts of the organism, as is the case for all higher animals. An even bigger problem looms in the case of higher plants where growth never stops. There is good evidence, for instance, that the giant sequoias keep growing and that the only thing limiting their size is that they eventually become so big the wind may fell them.

It might be more realistic to equate development with life history. It is like the old problem in logic of the definition of an individual: usually an individual is defined as an organism (as a rule an adult) in an instant of time. From a logical point of view the idea of taking the organism in a particular period of time seems cumbersome, and it would be better to consider an individual as the sum total of all the changes from fertilized egg to death. This definition of individual would then be the same as the definition we are proposing for development.

Evidence that genes act during the whole life history is excellent. From genetic studies there are genes known to affect the cleavage of the fertilized egg and all the early stages of development. There are genes, such as eye pigments in *Drosophila,* that act just as maturity is about to come into being; there are genes that operate in animals in latter life after the major growth phases have passed (balding in man). Even senescence, the aging of the body that results in an increased likelihood of death, is itself the result of gene activity and, therefore, selection. There is so far as we know no period of the life history, nor any change in the life history that is not under the direct control of genes.

Therefore, the first step in an understanding of development would be an understanding of how genes give their instructions, how they act. This is a subject of great interest among biologists at the moment, because there are many things we do not know about it. However, progress in the last decade has been rapid, and we do have some insights into the problem.

Since the gene is a chemical substance, what we should most like to know is what kind of chemical instructions it gives the cytoplasm. This field of biochemical genetics received a major push from the important discovery of G. W. Beadle and E. L. Tatum that genes that controlled specific steps in the synthesis of body constituents could be identified. They were wise in their choice of an organism, for the bread mold *Neurospora* can be grown on a very simple growth medium containing a few salts and sugars, and from these substances the mold synthesizes all its amino acids, vitamins, and other chemical constituents. By subjecting the spores to mutation-inducing radiation they found that some of the mutants were unable to grow on this so-called minimal medium. These mutants were then placed upon a complete or nutrient-rich medium, and if they grew, the supposition was that they had lost the ability to make some key substance and that this substance was present in the rich complete medium. A series of media were prepared each containing the minimal medium and one additional substance, an amino acid or a vitamin, for instance. If a mutant that was unable to grow on minimal medium alone could grow on a medium containing a particular amino acid, the obvious conclusion was that the mutant was incapable of performing that particular synthesis. In this way they identified a whole series of genes and were able to relate these directly to the synthesis of specific substances (Figure 13).

It was immediately realized that the reason the synthesis failed was that the enzymes involved were in some way inadequate. The importance of this is that what the genes control are the enzymes and that the enzymes in turn control the chemical steps occurring within a cell. These steps are not only concerned in the synthesis of amino acids and vitamins but also complex carbohydrates and proteins; in fact, as we have already seen, all the cell machinery, the cell energetics are run by enzymes. Any change in the enzymatic constitution of the cell is bound to produce a change in the character of the cell. Therefore, genes in turn control the key controlling agent of the cytoplasm.

In some cases it has been possible to find the genes governing the enzymes that mediate a whole series of steps towards the synthesis of one larger substance. This is done by first finding a number of mutations that can be reversed by the addition of the substance. Some of these, of course, may be identical mutations, but others may be affecting different enzymes in the chain of synthetic steps leading to the production of the substance. Each mutant can be tested by using different precursor substances that are known to be intermediate steps in the chain. If such an intermediate substance "cures" the mutant and if normal growth occurs on minimal

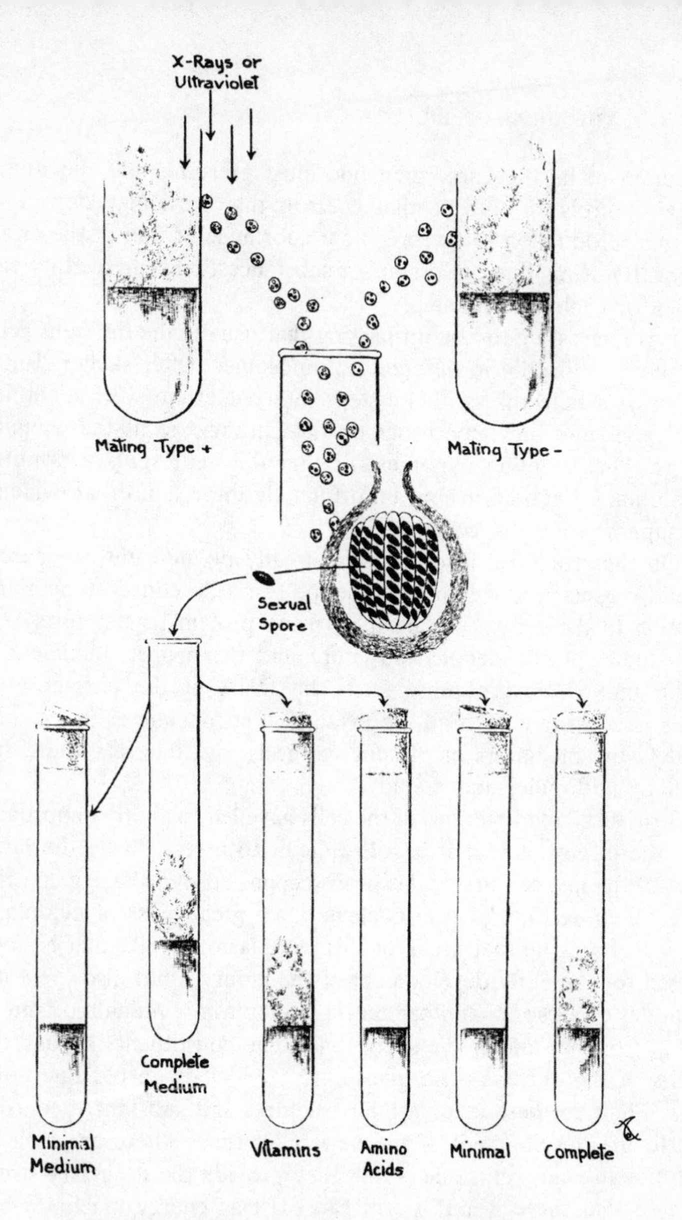

Fig. 13 Experimental procedure for the production and detection of biochemical mutants in *Neurospora*. In this case clearly the mutant has lost the ability to synthesize some vitamin. (After G. W. Beadle.)

medium in its presence, then one must presume that the mutant gene controls an enzyme that controls that particular step of the normal production of the precursor substance or one of the earlier steps. By using different precursor substances, one can identify each gene for each enzyme step.

It is interesting to note in passing that usually the different genes in such a series lie in different chromosomes helter-skelter. But in one case where the synthetic steps in a bacterium were identified, the genes had the same order on the chromsome as the chemical steps. The tempting hypothesis is that this represents a primitive evolutionary condition, but unfortunately there is no real evidence to support such a speculation.

On the structural level, as was already pointed out, we cannot identify gene products or see how the genes do convey their information to the enzymes. Enzymes, being proteins, must surely obtain their specific detailed structure and the proper alignment of their amino-acid groupings from the DNA of the chromosome. This is consistent with all the evidence that nucleic acids are ultimately the mediators of protein synthesis, but the details are still sketchy and under active study.

Structural investigations of the cells have led to another approach, but the importance of it is still difficult to assess. Since the latter part of the last century, it has been recognized that the egg contributes far more than just its nucleus but a great mass of cytoplasm as well. It is true that much of this cytoplasm is yolk, that is, food stored for the early development of the embryo; but also there are granules of all sorts—mitochondria, endoplasmic reticulum, and so forth. For that matter the sperm has some constituents beyond the DNA of the nucleus. The question is (and it is an old question) how much do these cytoplasmic structures and substances contribute to the development of the new individual? There are at least two possible answers: one is that they provide the necessary structure so that the egg and sperm can exist as energy machines but that the future development of the particles is, along with all else, under gene control. Another answer is that the cytoplasm contains some structures that have hereditary or gene properties of their own; that is, these plasma genes are carried continuously in the cytoplasm, they are capable of mutation, and they, like genes, control certain enzyme steps. There is evidence that some structures in the cell are continuous in this sense (the centrioles, so active during cell division, are cases in point), but we do not know how common and widespread this kind of genetic control of development might be.

One of the finest bits of evidence, besides all the genetic evidence that has been mentioned, that development is controlled by the activities of the nucleus comes from the work of J. Hämmerling on a rather peculiar alga called *Acetabularia.* It is a green marine alga, thin and delicate in structure, with a broad cap or hat; it gives the impression of a weird underwater daisy. Even though the whole plant will reach a size of 2 inches, it, nevertheless, has no cross walls and is a continuous tube. The most unusual aspect of its structure is that all its nuclei are concentrated in one large ball (which amounts to a giant nucleus) in the rootlike structure at its base. During the course of normal development or after the hat has been removed and regeneration occurs, the tip of the stalk first grows upward and then produces the radial spokes that make up the hat. If the nucleus is supposed to direct the details of this rather elaborate hat-forming process, is it not rather strange that the nucleus should be able to do this fine work yet be sitting 2 inches away? It would almost seem to be a case of development by remote control.

In some ingenious experiments Hämmerling showed that this was the case, and, furthermore, the experiments give us some insight as to how it occurs. In the first place if a piece of stalk is removed and separated from both its hat and its nucleus, it will live for some time and even show slight beginnings of hat formation, but no more than this. Fortunately there are various species of *Acetabularia* that have different shaped hats, and it is possible to graft the stem of one species onto the base of another the way one can graft different varieties of fruit trees or grape vines. Since there is the giant nucleus and little cytoplasm in the base, and since the stalk contains a large amount of cytoplasm, one can make a graft in which the cytoplasm is almost entirely from one species and the nucleus entirely from another. The graft will "take," and a new cap emerges. At first the regenerating hat shows signs of the stem or cytoplasm species, but these signs soon disappear, and the new cap takes on entirely the character of the species belonging to the nucleus. This means that the nucleus can direct the course of development not only 2 inches away but through the cytoplasm of another species. It is assumed that the nucleus gives off substances that pass through the cytoplasm. This would explain why the stem alone will show a few signs of regeneration, that is, until all the nuclear substances it contains are used up. And it would also explain why in the grafting experiment the beginning development is characteristic of the stem piece, for the cytoplasm of that piece still has nuclear substances left from its original nucleus (Figure 14).

One generalization to be made from these experiments is that developmental change seems to be something that the cytoplasm does, while the nucleus only directs the change. Another argument on this point frequently given is that all the nuclei in the body of a plant or an animal, such as ourselves, are roughly identical in appearance, yet we, for instance, have nerve, muscle, liver, and all sorts of different cell cytoplasms. If we limit the conclusion from these observations to the statement that morphological changes in development are manifest in the cytoplasm only, we will be on safe ground; but we do not know whether or not there might be internal chemical differences that we cannot see in the nuclei of different tissues.

The evidence that this might be the case comes primarily from some interesting experiments of R. Briggs and T. J. King on frog embryos. By microdissection they took single nuclei from small cells of different regions of a young embryo and injected the nuclei into a ripe egg, which had previously been enucleated. This egg, with its foreign nucleus, proceeded to develop, sometimes giving a normal embryo, sometimes an abnormal one. The important point is that if it gave an abnormal embryo and if the nuclei of this abnormal embryo were in turn injected into fresh eggs, they also produced abnormal embryos possessing the same abnormalities as their "parent." This can be repeated for another generation; the

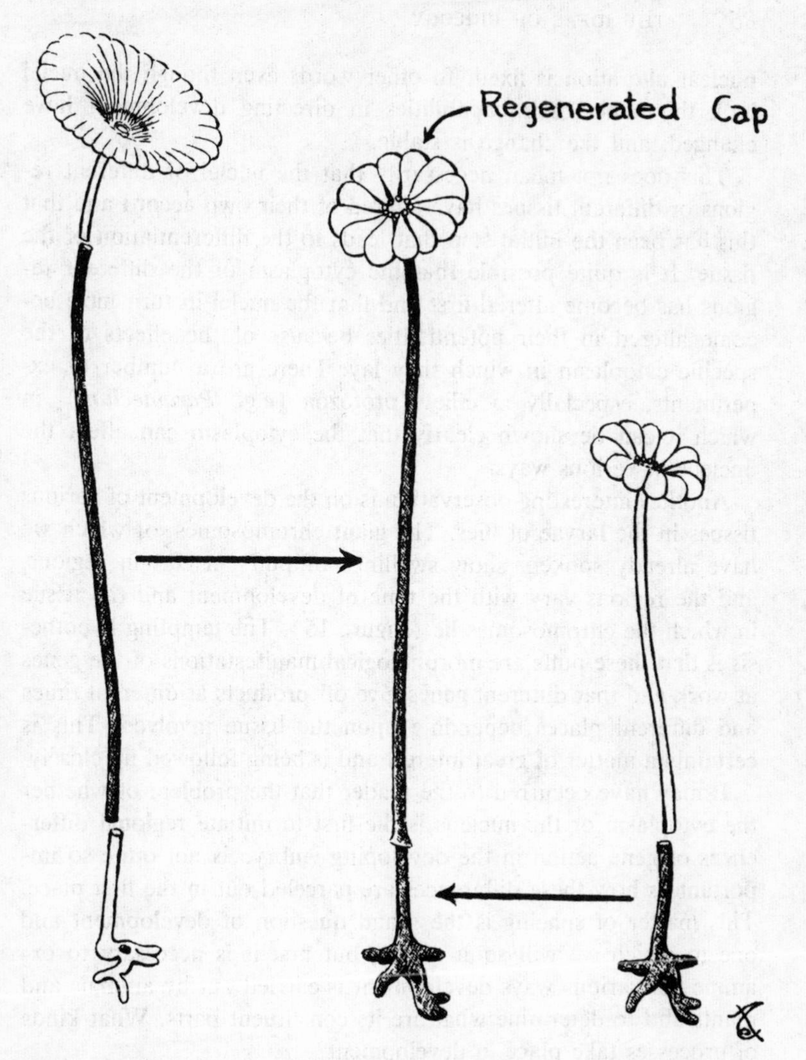

Fig. 14 Grafting experiment in *Acetabularia*. A piece of stalk consisting of cytoplasm only (left) is grafted onto a nucleus-containing rizoid of another species (right). The graft grows a new cap which has the character of the nucleated portion, indicating that the influence of the nucleus overrides that of the cytoplasm in determining the pattern of differentiation.

nuclear alteration is fixed. In other words even though the nuclei look the same, their capabilities in directing development have changed, and the change is stable.

This does not mean necessarily that the nuclei of different regions or different tissues have altered of their own accord and that this has been the initial step that leads to the differentiation of the tissue. It is quite possible that the cytoplasm of the different regions has become altered first and that the nuclei in turn have become altered in their potentialities because of the effects of the specific cytoplasm in which they lay. There are a number of experiments, especially in ciliate protozoa (*e.g., Paramecium*), in which it can be shown clearly that the cytoplasm can affect the nucleus in various ways.

Another interesting observation is on the development of various tissues in the larvae of flies. The giant chromosomes, of which we have already spoken, show swellings or puffs in certain regions, and the regions vary with the time of development and the tissue in which the chromosomes lie (Figure 15). The tempting hypothesis is that these puffs are morphological manifestations of the genes at work and that different genes give off products at different times and different places depending upon the tissue involved. This is certainly a matter of great interest and is being followed up closely.

It may have occurred to the reader that the problem of whether the cytoplasm or the nucleus is the first to initiate regional differences of gene action in the developing embryo is not quite so important as how these differences are parceled out in the first place. This matter of spacing is the grand question of development and one to which we will soon return, but first it is necessary to examine the various ways development is carried out by animals and plants and to determine what are its constituent parts. What kinds of processes take place in development?

There are as many different kinds of development as there are animals and plants, so it is difficult to obtain any comprehensive picture of how development occurs for organisms in general. The best that can be done is to try to see what basic elements make up development and in this way dissect or analyze the process. There are various ways this can be done, but a useful and simple one is

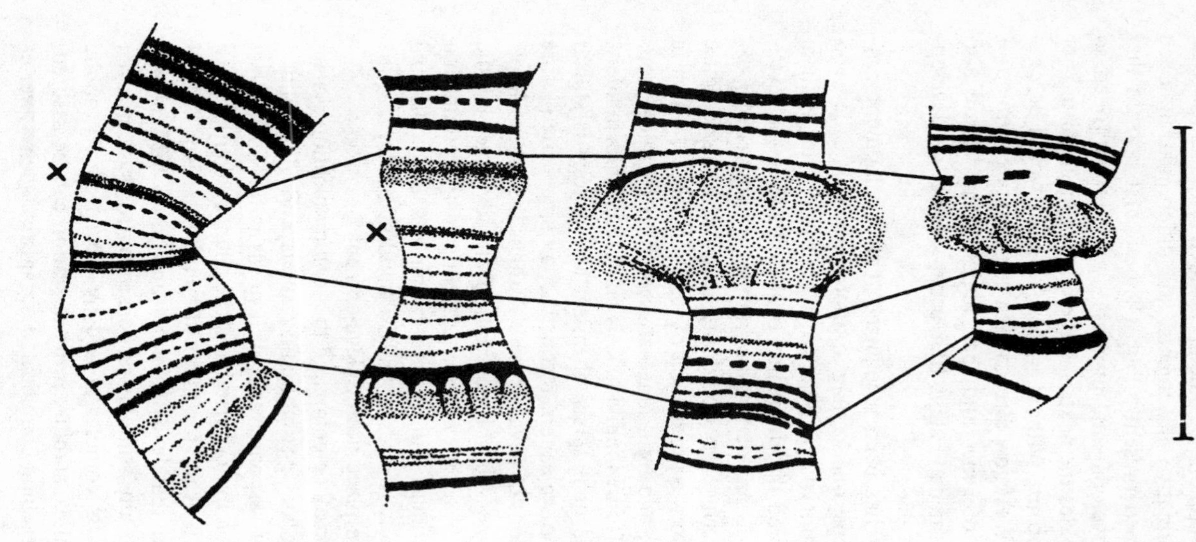

Fig. 15 The demonstration of puffs on the giant chromosomes of a fly. These are identical sections of one particular chromosome from different tissues and at different stages of development. The locations of identical genes are shown by the connecting lines, and it is clear that each chromosome has its characteristic band structure which presumably reflects the activities of the genes in the region. Notice especially the region marked "X" that shows a puff in the two right-hand chromosomes. (From W. Beerman.)

to consider that development is made up of three elements: growth, morphogenetic or formative movements, and differentiation. Each of these will be defined presently, but it should first be said that these constructive developmental processes must be controlled so one generation resembles the next, and the control mechanism is of the greatest interest to us. Without it, development would be chaotic and monstrous. We know already that the ultimate method of control is by means of genes and their actions, but we are also interested in the intermediate steps that occur during the developmental process.

For a long time it has been recognized that development consists of a series of steps, one leading to another. This is called epigenesis or causal embryology, and even Aristotle and William Harvey (who discovered the circulation of the blood) in the seventeenth century were aware of its importance. If we were to express it in modern terms, we would say that the genes produce substances that lead to the production of new substances, which in turn make a new set; and by a long series of such chemical steps the end product, the formed individual, is achieved. Unfortunately, however, at this stage of progress chemical embryology is still at a beginning phase, and we cannot reconstruct an epigenetic picture of the chemical reactions of development. Perhaps the best example of what has been done was the description already given of the gene-enzyme control of a series of steps leading to the production of one chemical substance. But despite its importance in showing us how the steps occur, it gives us only a handful of steps in the million that must take place during development.

These causal steps may be compared to a communication system in which there are successive stimuli and responses. Each condition is a system capable of response, and all it needs is the push to set it off. Once the reaction has occurred and the change taken place, a new response system is ready for the next stimulus. It is a kind of chemical conversation that leads to more and more far-reaching conclusions. And like any stimulus-response control system, even a man-made one, by its complexity and by the specificity of the stimuli and the responses, stability in its operation can be assured. This means that in large and complicated organisms, such as vertebrates, there must be many controlled steps; it is a communication system that would make a telephone exchange or an electronic calculator look childishly simple and inefficient by comparison.

Not all the steps need be small; there may be master controlling steps or communication systems that transcend the cells and guide parts or the whole of the developing embryo. This is the way in which the entire embryo can develop as a unit and its parts become properly spaced. Clearly these master controlling agents will be of special interest to us even though we may at the moment only have a rudimentary knowledge of them. Therefore, for each constructive aspect of development, growth, morphogenetic movement, and differentiation we will make a special search for these master controlling agents that are of such key importance in the epigenetic events from fertilized egg to maturity.

By growth we mean the synthesis of new protoplasm. In the case of a human being the fertilized egg is microscopic, a mere pinpoint; yet we ourselves are well over a hundred pounds of protoplasm. One of the events that goes with this increase in bulk is cell division, for cell size stays roughly constant within certain limits, and in human beings there are approximately forty cell generations ending up with about a million-million (10^{12}) cells. This means an increase not only in cytoplasmic mass and cell membranes but in nuclei and their constituent parts as well. If the problem is great for man, consider that of the blue whale, which may reach a length of 100 feet and weigh 150 tons.

Energy is needed for this massive synthesis and thus represents a problem in the beginning of development; before the animal embryo has produced a mouth and a feeding apparatus or the plant embryo has produced leaves with which it can photosynthesize and capture energy from the sun, it must have energy for growth. In both animals and plants this problem is met by the production of yolk (or its equivalent in plants), which is set aside in the egg. Yolk is no more than fuel, and it is steadily used up as the early embryonic stages proceed until finally energy is available from some other source. In invertebrates this may be by the feeding of the larva; in placental mammals this is by the implantation of the embryo on the wall of the uterus and the drawing of the nutrients from the mother through the circulation of the placenta into the embryo. Plants have an added feature in that they have two steps to the process. First the endosperm provides nutrients for the earliest embryonic stages; then a seed is formed, and the seed leaves or cotyledons are packed with nutrients so that the germinating seed will be able to become established before it is able to use sunlight. By the time the first leaves are expanded and functional, the cotyledons will be shriveled and depleted and will drop off.

If we now turn directly to the key problem of the control of growth, the most obvious kind of control is the cessation of growth with maturity. As has already been pointed out, this is not a universal phenomenon, for trees have a continuous growth, and to some extent (to the constant joy of the angler) fish continue to increase in size although their rate of increase falls off sharply. However, there are a number of cases known among plants where there does seem to be a fixed, inherited growth limit; and also among animals (for instance, birds and mammals definitely stop growing at a certain age). This over-all stoppage of growth in the case of vertebrates is due to the sealing off or calcification of the growth zones in the long bones, so that they can no longer increase in length. The cause is, therefore, quite specific in a particular tissue, and this does not mean that other parts of the body might not continue to increase in size. We may have reached the age where we no longer increase in height, but according to the bathroom scales we may be growing in other directions. To continue with mammals, there are many other examples of regional growth among their complex tissues. For instance, the blood cells are constantly destroyed and replaced by a growth process that continues unabated until death; hair and fingernails keep growing; and there are other examples. The moral from this is that growth is not a general increase of the whole mass in large plants and animals but a series of specific regional increases that are so carefully balanced as to give a well-proportioned individual.

In plants this regional control is effected partly by the growth zones or meristems. In a woody plant there are, first of all, apical meristems—one at the tip of each shoot and one at the tip of each root (*e.g.*, the onion root tip). These apical meristems are responsible for the increases in length. Inside the plant, usually in a cylinder just inside the bark, there is the lateral meristem or cambium, which is responsible for the increase in thickness of the tree. The cambium keeps splitting off cells; when they are split off to the inside they become wood (xylem), and when they are split to the outside they become bast (phloem). By varying the amount of growth in these respective zones it is possible to vary the over-all shape and proportions of the plant (Figure 16).

There are some animals, the colonial hydroids (*e.g., Obelia,* which is related to the noncolonial *Hydra;* they are all coelenterates), that are very plantlike in appearance. They form small bushes usually about 2 or 3 inches high and are found in the ocean, often on the pilings of wharfs. Other examples are the corals, which are close relatives. Their resemblance to plants goes below the surface, for they also have meristems. They do not have lateral meristems (unless the lateral calcium deposits of the corals be so considered, although this is not a growth of a living tissue but a mineral accretion), but they do have meristems responsible for the increase in length of the stalks. These may be either apical or intercalated somewhere along the stalk, usually just below one of the feeding polyps (Figure 16).

In the search for further control mechanisms, especially ones that transcend the cell boundaries, a great amount of important work has been done on growth hormones. In plants it was discovered that the activity of the growth zones was under the direct control of such hormones (which in plants are called auxins). But with the pursuit of these studies (which are being actively continued at the moment in many laboratories), it has slowly emerged that the relation of growth hormones to plant growth is a very complex one. In the first place there are the causes of the distribution of auxin to explain. Only certain parts of the plant produce it, and it travels to other parts in specific ways. Once its distribution is achieved, different parts of the plant respond in different ways to the auxin. In some regions a particular concentration of auxin will stimulate growth, while in other regions the same concentration will inhibit growth. Therefore, while auxin is a key factor in the growth

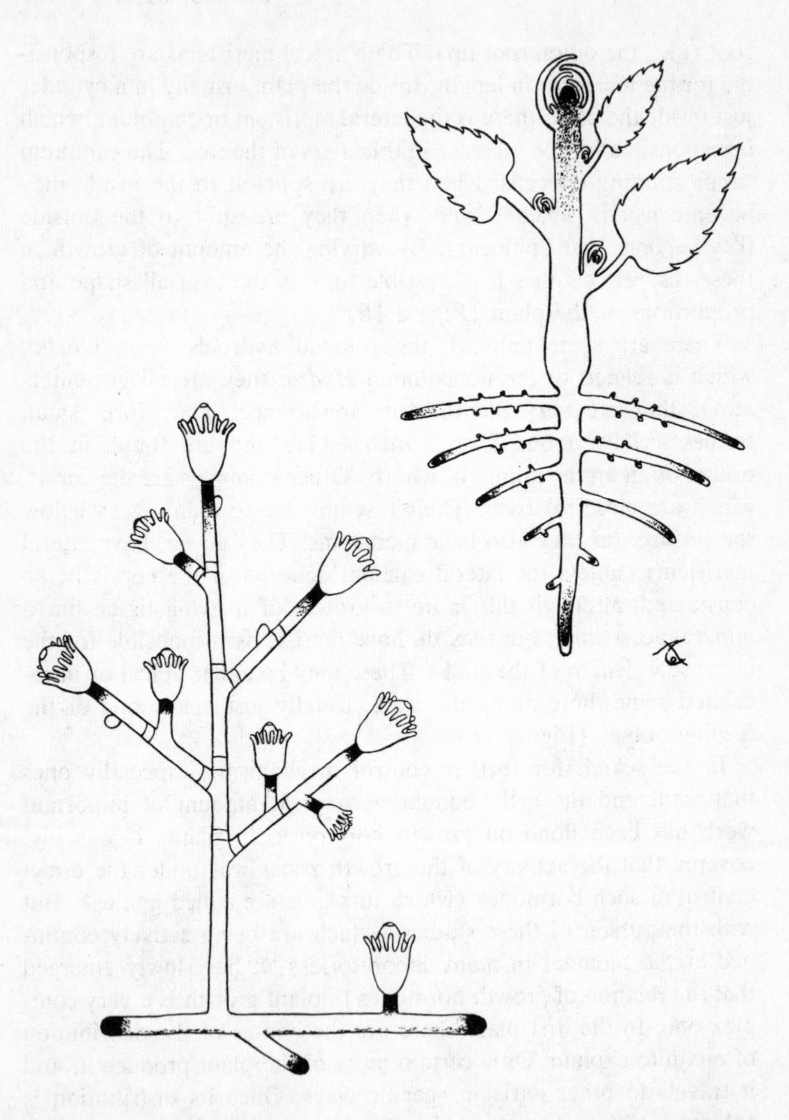

Fig. 16 A comparison of the apical growth zones or meristems in animals (left) and plants (right). The region of most active growth is indicated by the darker stippling. A colonial hydroid is shown on the left and a higher plant on the right. (After A. Kühn.)

patterns of a plant, it is clearly not the only factor, for we must also account for the spacing mechanisms that lead to its distribution in the plant, as well as for the spacing mechanisms that produce the different regional responses. Since these spacing mechanisms amount to differences in different parts of an organism, we will return to what little we know of the problem when we discuss differentiation.

Animals also have growth hormones. There has been some exceedingly interesting work recently done upon the growth hormones of insects, but our most thorough knowledge is that of the growth hormones of mammals. The principle hormone, called simply the growth hormone, is produced by the pituitary gland—that small, round pellet at the base of the brain that is the master control bureau for the entire mammalian hormone system. If any mammal has a deficiency in the production of this hormone a dwarf will be the result; on the other hand, if the pituitary gland should be tumorous or overdeveloped in some way, the result will be a giant. When we hear of human beings of 8 feet or more, we can be confident that this is the result of excess growth hormone. As a corollary to what was said before about long bones: if growth hormones are produced in excess after the bones have been sealed off and cannot elongate any further, then a peculiar warping of the facial features and of the hands will occur. This malformation, known as acromegaly, is because certain regions of the face and fingers still have cartilage that undergoes further expansion with the stimulus of the growth hormone.

Mammals have other hormones that affect growth. Thyroxin, produced by the thyroid gland, affects the rate of cell metabolism, and if there is a deficiency of thyroxin in infancy, a dwarf will result. In both these cases and with pituitary dwarfs, cures are possible with hormone injections. Excess of thyroxin does not produce giants but excitability and heightened metabolic activity. The sex hormones are also important in stimulating regional growth, the most extreme case being the annual formation of antlers in deer, which is specifically controlled by the male sex hormone. But in the case of animals we have the same ultimate problem that we encountered with plants: what causes the hormones to be produced in specific regions and in some cases to cause growth at specific regions? The question again is one of spacing.

One observation of considerable importance in this matter of the control of growth is that various regions of any growing organism, a plant or an animal, high or low on the scale of beings, have their specific growth rates, often ones that remain constant for extended periods of development. It is even possible to compare the growth rates of any two different parts, and obviously their ratio will remain constant if the two parts continue at a constant rate. This simple principle of relative growth (which can readily be expressed mathematically) may be illustrated by a number of examples. Take, for instance, the growth of the sword of a developing sailfish. At first this fish has hardly any bump at all, but as the over-all increase of the fry occurs the sword becomes progressively longer with respect to the body. If the rate of increase in length were the same for both the sword and the rest of the body, the tiny fry would have relatively long swords in perfect proportion to the rest of their bodies. If, on the other hand, the growth rate of the sword length exceeded that of the body length, then the sword could (as it actually does) begin relatively small and end up relatively long (Figure 17). Another example could be arm length versus body length in man. A small child puts his hands straight up, and they barely come above the top of his head. An adult seems almost gibbonlike by comparison and can reach a great distance above his head. Clearly the growth rate of the arm length far exceeds that of the head length. These examples have both used, for the sake of simplicity, length as a measure, but the principle applies equally well with the volume or weight of parts of an organism.

The importance of our consideration of relative growth is that it emphasizes that the whole shape of an organism can to some extent be determined by regional differences in growth rates. But in turn, what determines growth rates? How is it that one region grows at one rate and another, perhaps one close by, grows at a different rate?

The only kind of growth rate control that we know is genetic. This is mainly the work of R. Goldschmidt, who championed the

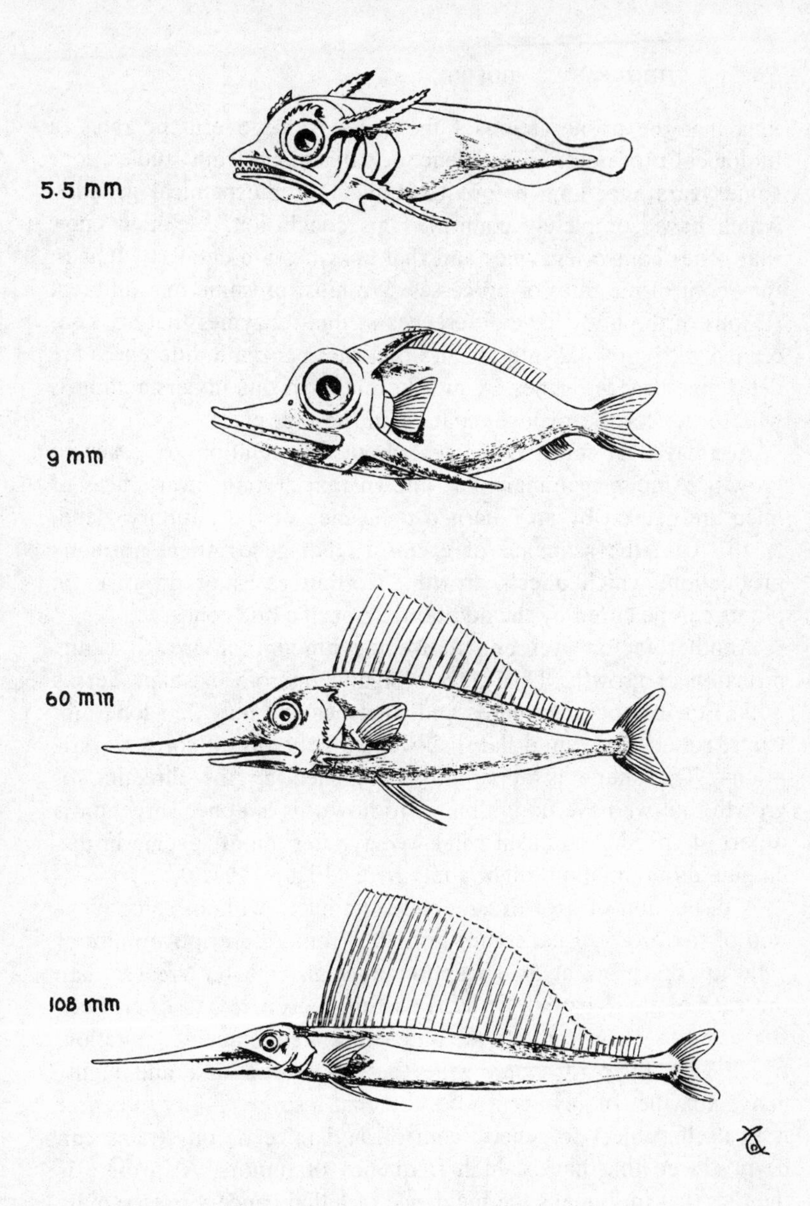

Fig. 17 Stages in the growth of a young sailfish. Note that as size increases, the snout extends more rapidly than the lower jaw. (After W. Beebe.)

idea that the prime action of the genes is to govern the rates of biological processes. His evidence for this came from studies done some years ago, long before the advent of biochemical genetics, which have completely confirmed his conclusion. We now know that genes control enzymes and that enzymes are catalysts, that is, they control the rates of processes. We must presume that different regions of the body have differences in their enzymes that are concerned with growth synthesis and that these enzyme differences are determined by the genes. Again the blank in our understanding is what produces the regional spacing in the first place.

A great deal more is known about the relation of genes to growth. Among mammals it is known that certain dwarf races of mice are caused by an inherited deficiency of the pituitary gland. In this case the sequence of events is that genes affect hormone production, which affects growth. Certain cases of dwarfism in plants can be cured by the addition of specific hormones.

Another factor over and above the amount of growth is the direction of growth. This plays a significant role in shape versus bulk. For instance, in gourds and squashes one may find long thin fruits, round fruits, and flat disk-shaped fruits in all sorts of variations. The shape is apparently controlled by the direction of growth, but we have no inkling as to how this is done. Direction is a part of spacing, so again what we say later about spacing in discussing differentiation might apply here (Figure 18).

A discussion of growth cannot be complete without some mention of tumorous or cancerous growth. From a descriptive point of view tumors grow at an exceptionally high rate far greater than the rate of their parent tissue. For this reason it has often been suggested that a cell in a tissue underwent a spontaneous mutation, which gave birth to a new gene that fostered a new and highly active enzyme. In any event we know that a susceptibility to cancer is in itself subject to genetic control, and mice or rat strains can be produced that have a high frequency of tumors. Also there is the fact that in humans the incidence of lethal cancers rises rapidly after the age of forty, and it is presumed that this occurred by natural selection; that is, it would be selectively disadvantageous to have a high incidence of lethal cancers before the reproductive or childbearing phase; but after, the effect on the production of offspring would be nil. Therefore, cancers appear in a later phase of life and the fact that this can be modified by selection in this way directly implies a genetic control of susceptibility.

The next major constructive process of development to consider is that of morphogenetic movements. These formative movements involve no increase in the amount of protoplasm, no synthesis but merely a redistribution of the shaping of what protoplasm there is. The movements are usually cellular, that is, the mass migration of cells; but there are some good cases of movement

Fig. 18 A variety of shapes among gourds and squashes.

within one cell or, at least, one cell wall. These occur in multinucleate organisms where there are no cross walls and also in the eggs of a number of invertebrates. In these eggs, there is a redistribution, a migration of granular material, usually following fertilization. It is known that this repositioning of cytoplasmic material has important consequences as far as the future development is concerned, for the various materials are the first steps in the production of regional differences in structure.

Morphogenetic movements hardly exist in any form in higher plants, because the cells are rigid and incapable of locomotion. In the lower plants, the fungi and the algae, there are many curious cases of stages of development having morphogenetic movement; but each seems special and a separate experiment of its own in the course of evolution. As a key process in development these movements only come into their own in the animal kingdom.

We have already mentioned the internal movements within the eggs of some invertebrates. The next and the most important movement of all animal morphogenetic movements (which is found in some form in all multicellular animals) is the gastrulation movement. It is basically the movement that makes a double cell layer out of a simple, single-celled ball of cells; it converts the blastula into the gastrula. This may occur by the inwandering of cells from the outside cell layer into the central cavity. This inwandering may be at one point or various points within the ball (*e.g.,* in the coelenterates). The most frequently illustrated type of gastrulation is that in which the ball of cells collapses so that the single-layered sphere turns into a double-layered hemisphere (*e.g.,* echinoderms, such as the sea urchin or starfish, and the primitive chordate *Amphioxus*). In vertebrates the yolk becomes far more highly developed, and gastrulation is cramped by this large inert mass. In frogs and other amphibians the cells wander in and about the yolk at one end region while in fish, birds, and reptiles, whose yolks are very large, the embryo becomes spread out as a sort of cap on the yolk, and gastrulation becomes two dimensional, with one sheet of cells passing under another. In placental mammals even though the yolk is diminished, this kind of flat gastrulation is also present as a leftover from its yolky ancestry.

Besides sundry other lesser morphogenetic movements, such as the migration of cells to specific points in the beginning of limb formation, vertebrates have one other major movement. This is the closing of the neural folds (neurulation) that occurs some time after gastrulation.

As with growth the important question here is how are these movements controlled? How are the cells guided so that each generation they make the same twists and turns? In the case of the redistribution of cytoplasmic material within the egg of invertebrates, it has been presumed that there are diffusion gradients, perhaps set up by the sperm entrance, that are responsible for the movements of the particles. In the case of gastrulation it has been noted that the cells of the surface are all connected to a material that covers the whole embryo. This surface coat, as it is called, is capable of contraction and expansion and literally guides the amoebalike cells in their movement. This is understandable, because we know that amoebae and embryonic cells are extremely sensitive to respond to the orientation of the structure they are crawling upon, and they react to any pull tensions, however delicate. Also there is evidence, in some cases of morphogenetic movements, of a chemical guidance of the cells. The cells respond to a chemical gradient and go towards the point of high concentration. They are, in essence, guided by smell just the way insects are guided to a flower by its scent.

A new and particularly intriguing experimental approach to morphogenetic movement has opened up recently, although the full implications of it for normal development are not yet clear. The procedure is to take the cells from a developing embryo and by various means separate them into a cell suspension. The cells should be properly marked so that they may be identified from the very beginning of the experiment. The suspension will fall to the bottom of a dish if placed in a suitable medium, and the cells soon wander about. If one started with a mixture of precartilage and premuscle embryonic cells, one would expect a random mixture of the two. This is exactly what does not happen, for the end result is a ball of cartilage surrounded by a ball of muscle. Since the cells are marked, it can be proved that all the cells retained their original fate and that somehow, in the gathering mass of cells, the precartilage cells came together in the center and the premuscle cells sorted out and surrounded the cartilage. It means that the cells in their movements can recognize other cells, either stick to them or not, and find their proper position in the whole mass. If these remarkable cell properties are not used in normal development in some way, it would seem most surprising.

In all the cases of morphogenetic movements as they occur in the embryo, we again are faced with a major spacing problem. The movements themselves involve one region migrating towards or away from another, and there must somehow be a master pattern, a master plan to the whole embryo. It is not enough to say that the surface coat guides the cells; we then immediately want to know what laid down the surface coat in its particular configuration. It is not enough to say that genes are responsible for all these properties and their subsequent movements; we want to know how genes produce these over-all patterns. Morphogenetic movements provide many examples of extracellular communication, in which they respond to external surface coats and chemical gradients and can even recognize different cell types. The question is: how are all these extracellular communication systems bound together to give a consistent pattern from generation to generation?

We can, at least, discuss this problem directly in the consideration of differentiation although we will have to admit that our ignorance of it far exceeds what we know. By differentiation we mean simply that differences appear in different parts of the embryo. These differences must ultimately be differences in chemical composition.

One of the characteristics of differentiation is that it can occur on different levels. For instance, there can be differentiation within a cell, and an example of this was provided when we talked of the movements of granular material within the egg of some invertebrates after fertilization. After the granules have come to rest, different parts of the fertilized egg definitely have different chemical compositions. It is also possible to speak of cellular differentiation in which a cell as a unit takes on a particular constitution. This kind of differentiation is so obvious that examples are hardly necessary, but in animals we need only think of muscle, nerve, or cartilage cells, and we could mention phloem or xylem cells in plants. Differentiation also occurs on the tissue and organ levels, and one can think of muscle and nerve for the one and the kidney or the brain for the other. The ultimate level of differentiation is traditionally thought to be the whole organism, although we shall see in the next chapter that this is not so, for there can be a super-differentiation in the form of social groups.

If the problem of differentiation of the organism as a whole is considered, then we come directly onto the spacing problem. How are the different parts established in such a balanced way that each generation a perfect, whole organism is manufactured? Before even beginning to say anything directly about this, let us first describe some circles around the problem.

As can be seen from the examples given, the chemical differences of parts associated with differentiation pertain to different functions. In other words differentiation is the result of division of labor, and each part through chemical change becomes specialized in performing some specific function. The wonder lies in the fact that this divided labor can be so consistently well proportioned or parceled out in an individual. Since all biological phenomena arise as a result of selection, perhaps it would be well to consider this organism differentiation from this point of view. If a large multicellular mass of cells is to effectively compete with other organisms, it must function smoothly. If its internal labor is divided, clearly this division is brought about solely because of the need of effective competition. We assume that the reptiles supplanted the amphibians and that the mammals supplanted the reptiles as the dominant forms because of very slight improvements in their division of labor. Therefore, the selection pressure to have both an effective division of labor and especially to have it well controlled, well balanced (for else it would not even operate) is very strong indeed. So we can, at least, say that well-spaced, well-balanced differentiation has been cultivated by strong selective forces although this hardly tells us how mechanically it can come into being.

From a descriptive point of view, early developing embryos fall into two classes. There are those in which all the parts are equivalent or equipotential, and this means that if the embryo is cut in two, each part has all the potentialities and can produce a complete embryo. In contrast to this regulative development, some embryos are mosaic, that is, at an early stage the different parts are no longer equipotential, and surgery will simply produce abnormal half embryos. Contrary to the views expressed at the turn of the century, it has been known for a long time that these are not different kinds of development but different stages in the development of all organisms. In animal embryos (surprisingly these studies have not yet been made with plant embryos) the beginning of development is characterized by a period of equipotentiality. This may stop at fertilization or even slightly before or it may continue until gastrulation. In any event the moment finally comes when there is a switch, and the equipotentiality of parts is lost. Even though the chemical details of these steps are lacking, there is probably no great mystery to the actual switch. Parts of the embryo are undergoing the beginning of differentiation, and the chemical changes eventually reach a stage where they can no longer go back. The process of change is sufficiently complicated so that it becomes irreversible. And this shift from regulative to mosaic development may occur early or late depending upon the species. In some species, such as the ascidians (sea squirts), a long period of mosaic development is followed by a larval stage in which a high degree of equipotentiality returns. So the irreversibility here is only temporary—during the period of the major construction of the embryo.

These facts are only moderately helpful in revealing the mechanism of controlled differentiation. They show simply that a period of equivalence of parts changes into a period of differences of parts; but perhaps more importantly, they show that these differences do not necessarily arise as a result of specific substances migrating into different regions (although this certainly happens in some cases) but rather that each part has all the possibilities, and certain ones are called forth in particular regions. Therefore, in order to have any insight into the controlled spacing of these differences, it is necessary to look to extracellular communication systems. Clearly the different parts of the developing embryo can communicate with one another so that each region does something in proportion to the activity of the other parts. What do we know of stimulus-response systems that transcend the cell, pervade the embryo, and control the orderly spacing?

I suppose the proper answer would be to admit that what we know is far too little. However, there are a number of such communication systems that have been intensively studied, and they constitute the most significant advances in embryology of the twentieth century. They could be roughly classed as polarity, gradients, and induction; but, as will be clear shortly, these are not mutually exclusive categories.

Polarity refers to the fact that all developing systems have some sort of directional quality to them—a head and a tail (or root and shoot), as well as secondary polarities, such as the dorsoventral and mediolateral axes for bilaterally symmetrical forms. This is merely a description of a geometric condition, and the physicochemical causes of this condition may be diverse. There is, for instance, evidence that a gradient of some substances will produce polarity, as well as a crystal-like orientation of the larger molecular components. Polarity is a universal element of developing systems, and it is presumed to be some kind of observable manifestation of an inner spacing mechanism. What these mechanisms might be is only known definitely in a few cases. The study of polarity reveals how much we still need to know of extracellular communication systems within an embryo.

Gradients are specific physical phenomena that we can observe and measure and are not a general category of ignorance, as was true of polarity. There are many known instances of gradients in developing systems in which some substance or group of substances is progressively more abundant in one part of the embryo than another. There is even the well-known case of the sea-urchin embryo (an echinoderm related to a starfish) in which there is a double gradient—one starting at one pole of the egg and diffusing southward and the other starting at the opposite pole and diffusing northward. Many details of the chemical differences, as well as the metabolic differences, of these two gradients are known, and it has been demonstrated that these gradients are ultimately responsible for at least the major regional differentiations. A gradient depends upon diffusion, and it is possible, considering the fact that the embryo is encased in an outer membrane, to balance the gradients delicately within the mass. Diffusion is clearly a means of extracellular communication, and the gradients that result are capable of leading to the balanced spacing with which we are so concerned. But we are still woefully ignorant of all the steps of the process even for any one organism.

More is known of the details of induction than any other of the communication systems. It was first discovered and fully appreciated by H. Spemann in the early part of this century. He showed that if a specific region (the dorsal lip of the blastopore) of an amphibian embryo at the gastrula stage was implanted upon the flank of another embryo, a whole new embryo would be induced by the graft and give rise to a twin embryo. At first Spemann thought that the dorsal lip region had special embryo-making properties, and he gave the region the grand name of "organizer"; but later one of his students, J. Holtfreter, showed that the dorsal lip was still capable of induction after it had been boiled! This and other experiments made it clear that the induction was by means of a chemical substance that stimulated the adjacent cells to respond, and the response was the production of a whole new embryo. Even though this has been known for more than thirty years, we still do not know the chemical identity of the inductor substance, for it turns out that the effect can be imitated by many chemicals. It is now thought that these chemicals cause a mild local breakdown of some of the cells and that the damaged cells release the key substance. This makes any chemical analysis very frustrating, because it is impossible to be sure if one has the key substance or something that stimulates the production of the key substances.

From our point of view here the important thing is that we have a clear-cut, extracellular stimulus-response system. This is by no means the only induction that takes place in the amphibian embryo, but it is followed by many lesser regional ones; induction is a widespread phenomenon. Even in plants the activities of the growth hormone auxin could be accurately compared with animal induction. The main difference centers around the fact that, thus far, animal inductions do not seem to be mediated by diffusion. Usually direct contact is necessary, although C. Grobstein has shown recently that if two regions are separated by a porous membrane, the inductive stimulus can pass through, provided that the holes in the membrane are sufficiently large to let pass some sort of fibrous, extracellular material.

This brief survey of what we know of transcendent stimulus-response systems that are responsible for the spacing within the developing embryo is indeed pitiful when one puts it up alongside of what needs to be known for a complete understanding. This is why the subject of development is considered to be in a very primitive state in terms of scientific elucidation, and it is for this reason that today many biologists are concentrating their research efforts in this direction.

The point has been made that development is adaptive both as far as itself is concerned and as far as its end product is concerned. Also it is presumed that all the steps of development are ultimately controlled by the genes. In some cases, such as induction, we can only presume that such control exists, for there are no experiments to prove that this is so. Assuming, nevertheless, that they all are gene controlled, this means that selection can operate on genetically determined characters that are part of the developmental sequence of events. In other words this paragraph has made full circle, for selection operates by culling genes, and any step of the life history can be as adaptive as any other.

This may have some considerable consequences as far as evolution is concerned that we have not as yet examined. Size and, therefore, development arose as adaptations, and once both were well established evolutionary changes had automatically a large bank of genes from which to pick and choose and alter. Change needs not only concern the adults, and phylogeny is no longer (as it is to a great extent in single-celled organisms) a succession of adults but a succession of life histories.

The significance of this conclusion can be seen in many ways. For instance, it is well known that among insects in some related forms the adults will be barely distinguishable, but the larvae will be so totally different in appearance that the adult affinity is hard to believe. Here there has been a change to the middle of the life history that is quite lost by the time the adult stage is reached.

A more general principle is that of heterochrony, in which different normal developmental processes or stages in the life histories change their relative time of appearance or disappearance. This again is properly understood in terms of genes. Two things can be varied: the time at which a gene acts and the rate of the process it controls (which is, after all, the prime function of the gene in any event). Therefore, the gene complex can, by varying the timing of its parts, produce all sorts of developmental schedules. For instance, in the rabbits or conies the young are born hairless and blind, while in the related hares the young are born fully clothed in fur and quite capable of taking care of themselves. The adaptive reason is undoubtedly related to the fact that hares have nests on the exposed surface of the ground while the rabbits have deep burrows. From the point of view of how this genetic change occurred, one can assume that the relative duration of pregnancy was extended in the hares so that their young would be brought forth in a condition enabling them better to cope with their perilous and exposed position on the top of the ground.

Some of these gene-controlled shifts in timing, these heterochronies, have far-reaching consequences. The most notable is neoteny in which, for one reason or another, the gonads and their production of egg and sperm mature relatively sooner than the rest of the animal. In other words an organism possessing embryonic or larval structures will be mature sexually.

A well-known example of a neotenous animal is the mud puppy, the large newt called *Necturus.* As a true amphibian it has a larval tadpole stage, but it never proceeds any further, for the larva is sexually mature. The Mexican axolotl is an interesting intermediate case. This newt has the same capabilities, but it can also under the proper circumstances metamorphose into a conventional adult and replace its gills with lungs.

The discovery of neoteny has raised the intriguing possibility that this could account for some of the large jumps or gaps in the evolution of the major groups. The classic example is the evolution of the vertebrates. It is known that the larvae of echinoderms closely resemble those of primitive chordates, but their adult stages are totally dissimilar. The hypothesis has been suggested that an ancestral echinoderm became sexually mature by neoteny and evolved along separate lines to give rise to the hemichordates. The evidence to support this hypothesis comes from the fact that the larvae of the two groups are remarkably similar even though the adults appear totally different.

Another point made previously that should be repeated here concerning phylogeny and its relation to development is that the sooner a gene mutation creates a viable change in the development of an organism, the more likely the change will be of major structural signifiance. It is only those gene changes that are acted upon at the end of development, such as eye color, that can have minor effects. Therefore, if one were to favor the notion that giant or megamutations have occurred and are responsible for major bits of evolutionary progress, one should imagine that these mutations are ones timed for an early stage of development.

In summary, it should be stressed that it is only possible to understand development in the framework of evolution and genetics. Evolution through selection has been the over-all guiding principle; genetics and its sexuality, the method by which selection could operate effectively; and development being the life history, the period of gene action that is the material from which selection can pick and choose. The three areas are all part of one great system.

Development itself, besides being a period of gene action, is a period of complex, stepwise (epigenetic) reactions in which the conditions of one step cause the next. Along with maintaining the cell energy machine to make all this possible, there must be signals and stimuli-and-response systems of sufficient complexity and specificity to ensure stability. The functioning of an organism and its development are all one; it has been hammered out by selection, and because the reproduction must occur in unicellular units, it involves a rapid and consistent unfolding each generation.

CHAPTER 5

SIMPLE TO COMPLEX

We have been constantly reminded of the fact that during the course of evolution organisms have proceeded from simple to the complex, from small to large; in the last chapter the consequences of this shift as far as development is concerned have been examined. It is evident that development, a period of gene action, involves a complex series of stimulus-response steps and that many of these extend beyond the confines of the cell wall to integrate the whole embryo.

But these extracellular communication systems extend far beyond the embryonic period and into the whole period of development, the whole life history. In the earlier embryonic period they are primarily concerned with internal construction, while during the later phases of the life cycle, when the adult stage is reached, they are primarily concerned with the integrated function of the organism. Again as a rule, the larger the organism, the more complex the communication system.

This is really the field of anatomy and physiology, and no attempt will be made here to do more than refer to a few general principles and give a few scattered examples, for this is a vast subject with large volumes full of details.

The functions of an organism are the same as those of a cell: (1) They must convert energy in order to keep the motor running. This might simply be referred to as feeding, which is certainly one of the important steps in the processing of energy into living activities. (2) They must reproduce, and while the majority of reproduction is sexual, there are also various kinds of asexual budding and fission. (3) They must have some kind of coordination. When discussing the cell we referred to this as irritability, for this is one important aspect—the sensitivity to external stimuli. But besides receiving the stimuli, organisms must convey them to different parts of the organism; the word coordination might be preferable in that it refers to all phases of awareness and response to immediate environmental situations.

In the case of the cell and, therefore, the single-celled organism we have already seen how this triumvirate—feeding, reproduction, and coordination—is handled. With the advent of multicellularity and the various radiating lines of progress, there has been some degree of specialization, and it may be useful to first consider how plants in general perform these three functions.

Feeding is primarily done by photosynthesis, and there are a number of structural and functional aspects to this method of energy intake. For instance, the sun-catching itself has various aspects. To begin with there is the progressive refinement of leaf anatomy so that the photosynthesis can be more effectively carried out. There is a vertical placement of the cells in the upper half of the leaf to form the palisade layer and the loose construction of the lower half, the spongy layer, to facilitate the entrance of carbon dioxide, the essential ingredient, along with water, for the manufacture of sugars. The lower epidermis is perforated with holes, the stomata, which are even provided with adjustable slit openings, for the guard cells open and close depending upon the humidity of the surrounding air.

The leaf itself must be in the optimum position to receive the sun. This is obtained both by the growth pattern of the whole plant, so that leaves have a minimum degree of overlap, and in some species by the movement of the leaves themselves, so that the leaf remains perpendicular to the sun's rays and in this way receives the largest amount of radiation.

Besides sun-catching there are many other activities associated with feeding and the conversion of energy by the plant. For example, there is the problem of taking in water, salts, and especially nitrogenous substances that are urgently needed for the synthesis of amino acids and proteins. This is done by the root, a structure, which by nature of the root hairs and other anatomical features, is admirably suited to pull in these substances from the soil. The substances must be transported to the leaves and other parts of the plant, and the carbohydrates manufactured in photosynthesis must be moved to all the living and growing parts of the plants. For the upward movement from the roots there are the tubes that run up the xylem, and the carbohydrates are primarily transported in the tubes of the phloem. By this system of transportation the manufacturing of sugars, the photosynthesis, can take place in one restricted spot, the leaves; and absorption takes place in one restricted spot, the root, yet the whole plant can metabolize and grow. There has been a division of labor, a specialization far more advanced than anything to be found among the green algae.

But not all plants feed by photosynthesis. Fungi take in dissolved substances directly through their thin hyphae by diffusion (exactly in the same manner as the root hairs of vascular plants). Some plants are parasites and send special rootlike absorbing structures into another plant. Most surprising of all are the predaceous plants. Some fungi, by means of snares and other lethal devices, trap small nematode worms and various protozoa. Among higher plants there are the insect eaters, such as the pitcher plant, which looks like a toy saxophone. Flies, once inside the delicious, carrion-reeking interior, are imprisoned by down-pointed hairs and slippery walls so that they ultimately drown and die in the soup at the base. Digestive enzymes are secreted and the broken down molecules absorbed into the tissues of the plant. The Venus's-flytrap has a clever trigger device in which two spiked, hinged leaves swing together rapidly (like an iron maiden); and *Drosera,* the honeydew, has drops of sticky liquid that trap and kill the fly at the hairlike tips of its leaves.

As far as the anatomy and physiology of plant reproduction is concerned, we find in higher plants that the most important factor is the lack of motility of the organism. Therefore, there are numerous devices to insure the dispersal of seeds and to insure the transfer of pollen from one plant to another. This has produced flower color, scent, and the extraordinary dual relationship between flowers and insects (as well as between flowers and some birds). Usually the flower is a source of food, of nectar for the insects; but there is the notorious case of an orchid whose transfer of pollen is effected by a particular wasp attempting to copulate with the flower. In anticipation of some comments that will be made further on, one can see in these flower-insect relations an extension of the stimulus-response system to include more than one species. This interspecific communication is clearly of great selective advantage to both forms and a key to cross-fertilization in immobile plants. The plants have compensated for their immobility by taking advantage of the locomotory powers of animals.

If one were to continue a list of the features connected with reproduction, one would have to make a detailed analysis of flower anatomy and the processes of gamete formation and fertilization. Also there are the interesting examples of vegetative reproduction in which runners or buds of various sorts can be sent out in all directions. And if the algae and fungi were also considered, there would be a mass of different types of asexual reproduction, as well as further variation in the mode of sexual reproduction.

Again because of the lack of motility, plant coordination is a very rudimentary affair. There are, of course, some movements, such as leaves or flowers following the sun in the sky; but these simple responses are by means of changes in the water content and, therefore, the turgidity on different sides of the plant. There are also growth movements, and these respond to light (as grass grown in a window box convincingly shows), as well as to gravity. The fact that shoots grow away from the center of the earth is clearly demonstrated by a stand of spruce on the steep side of a hill; roots have the reverse response and grow toward the center of the earth. These growth movements are known to be mediated by the uneven distribution of the growth hormone auxin, which somehow is concentrated in some spots and diluted in others by the action of light and gravity. Another growth response in plants is to touch or to contact, and this is exhibited in a striking way by the tendrils of vines. The best method of observing their growth is by time-lapse photography; the young tendril will weave back and forth as it extends, and should it hit a twig or a wire in this weaving, it will rapidly wind around it in a tight coil. There are also a few cases in which touch causes a sudden change in permeability of the cell, and, as in a released spring (or a punctured tire), there is a sudden movement. The fly triggering the leaf of Venus's-flytrap is an example and mimosa the sensitive plant, another.

If we turn to animals, the variety of ways in which the three functions are carried out is much greater. Compared to animals, plants are a more homogeneous group. For instance, the only kind of feeding that animals cannot perform is photosynthesis, but when it comes to taking in organic matter, they have evolved an elaborate series of different kinds of feeding devices; they can eat everything from soup to dry flour, from fetid carrion to sweet nectar, from woolen blankets to seven-course dinners with three wines.

Since all their food is either solid or liquid, there must be devices to take it into the body. The focal structure is the mouth and its attendant parts. Liquid feeders may have needlelike syringes, as in the mosquito or nectar-eating moths (that can unroll their rubbery syringes), or they may have two long jaws that come to a delicate point and allow the hummingbird to reach the nectaries of a flower and drink up the sugar. In the case of vegetarians, in which the plant material is hard to obtain because of all the cellulose that locks up the inner protoplasmic juices, grinding jaws of some variety are frequently found. Among mammals the flat, ridged teeth of sheep, horses, and cows are excellent examples (along with the regurgitation of the food to the back molars for a little extra cud-chewing). By contrast carnivorous mammals have sharp, pointed teeth to hold and tear the flesh, and even the beaks of birds of prey serve this function. Besides teeth there are sharp talons and claws to help hold and dismember. Insect-eating is a particular specialty of many animals. There are the flycatchers and the swallows, the woodpeckers that seek fat grubs in the cracks under the bark of trees, the tick birds that sit on the backs of water buffaloes to feast on the fat parasites that crawl over those huge beasts. Among mammals there are the various anteaters that tear termite nests apart with great claws and shoot their sticky tongues down the tunnels slapping the hundreds and thousands of termites into their mouths. Were we to continue with examples of different kinds of diets and mouth structures among vertebrates we could stay busy for a long while, and if we were to list all the invertebrates and all their pecularities as well, the subject would be eternally long. All that is important here is that the variety be stressed.

Once the food is taken in it must be processed—broken down to its constituent chemical parts and taken into the system. Again among invertebrates the variety of food processing is large, but here the brief mention of one example will be sufficient. Vertebrates all have roughly similar alimentary tracts, and even in the mouth the salivary glands secrete saliva, which both facilitates the passage of food and provides enzymes for the breakdown of starches. The massive production of extracellular enzymes to mediate the breakdown of food is one of the specialities of animal gut canals in general. There are also special muscles to push the food along the tube, and they operate so that the tube relaxes in front of the food and contracts behind. The system works perfectly under normal circumstances, although it does have an unfortunate tendency to go into reverse on the high seas. In the stomach there are both a muscular grinding and a battery of enzymes that attack various foods and, especially, begin the breakdown of proteins. When the food passes into the small intestine it receives the digestive juices of both the pancreas and the bile. Besides furthering food breakdown, the bile salts are interesting in that they facilitate the passage of fatty acids (the breakdown products of fats) through the intestinal wall into the blood stream. The passage of the dismembered food into the blood through the highly vascular projections into the gut canal (the villi) is one of the prime functions of the small intestine.

From this we become aware that to put these elementary fuel particles into all the cells of the body, it is necessary to have a transportation system. The blood system not only performs this function but also brings the oxygen to the tissue so that the fuel can be consumed. The specialization of the gut system could not have occurred without the development of a circulatory system. Then this large machine accumulates many wastes. The carbon dioxide escapes early into the blood and from there to the lungs or gills. The nitrogen wastes are more difficult to eliminate, and the incredibly elaborate kidney has evolved that deals specifically with waste elimination as a sort of blood filter.

The simple problem of taking in food has become, with increasing size, complexity, and efficiency of the organism, an extraordinarily elaborate one. It should always be kept in mind that each of these remarkable structures, with its equally remarkable function, came into being by natural selection, by virtue of mutation, recombination by sexuality, and the selection of the genes—genes that modified or controlled the development in these particular directions. Furthermore, we saw in the case of development that these structures were brought about by a series of stimulus-response steps, and now that they are functional they continue, even in their integrated operation, to be composed of a stimulus-response system. The sight or smell of food results in its capture by muscle movements, the use of claws and all the mouth structures. The presence of food stimulates the salivary glands, which respond by secretion. The food is pushed downward by controlled muscular activity. Its presence in the stomach acts as a stimulus for enzyme secretion and muscular grinding. We could go on and on with each step and show that it involves a stimulus and a response and that one step is dependent upon the previous one. The interdependence of parts, their proper integration are essential adaptations for the smooth and successful operation of an individual organism.

Except for a number of invertebrates animals are generally not hermaphroditic but have separate males and females. This particular characteristic of their reproduction, it was noted earlier, is probably correlated with their ability to move and wander about. The matter of bringing the egg and the sperm together in successful fertilization has many facets, but at the moment let us omit courtship and display and concentrate upon the anatomical-physiological aspect of fertilization. One of the successful evolutionary changes that is found among various invertebrate groups, as well as in vertebrates, is the devising of internal fertilization in which the sperm can be directly introduced into the female. This has been facilitated by the evolution of two structures that are complementary so that a successful union can be effectively achieved. In some insects that possess a hard exoskeleton the fine structure of the genitalia results in a most exact fit; with the softer tissues of higher vertebrates, this problem is more easily solved. However, in the majority of birds, while there always is internal fertilization, there are no special structures, and fertilization depends upon the more difficult and hazardous apposition of the cloacal openings.

The interesting thing is that here has been a co-ordinated selection in which the progressive change has occurred simultaneously in the male and the female, and for each the change has been in the opposite direction from the other. Males and females, of course, can be litter mates and have the same parents; but in the special sex chromosomes, the ones that determine the sex, different factors that affect anatomical structures are built up for each sex. Selection not only can produce single structures but complementary double structures in opposite sexes of the same species.

Once the egg and the sperm have come together, the fertilization process involves a complex series of chemical stimuli and responses that still are not completely understood. The egg produces a substance that affects the sperm and that causes the sperm to produce a substance that in turn affects the egg; by means of such a long, causal chemical conversation fertilization finally takes place. The degree of elaboration of the events leading to and mediating fertilization are not necessarily more complex as one proceeds upward in the animal kingdom, but many invertebrates, with the sponges probably taking first prize, have an exceedingly complex fertilization ceremony.

To make it clear that reproduction is not an isolated and remote event from the rest of the organism's functions, one should remember that one of the results of internal fertilization is that the young must be carried internally and that there are many accompanying anatomical changes needed. Also the proper male and female roles in fertilization and child-rearing are dependent upon the sex hormones, which stimulate the sex urge, maternal care, and milk production. The sex hormones are also significant in puberty by stimulating the production of the secondary sexual characteristics that often make male and female morphologically so distinct. It is again possible to show that the activity of reproduction also involves a highly integrated series of stimuli and responses.

As far as co-ordination in animals is concerned, we find that the variety and their total achievement vastly exceed what was found in plants. Again the difference no doubt is correlated with the ability of an animal to move. Muscular contraction is such an effective means of rapidly performing work that unless these movements are co-ordinated, the result would be violent chaos and probably self-destruction as well. The co-ordination of muscle is effected first by nerves that permit impulses or signals to be passed along them and then the centralization of these nerves in a co-ordination center, a kind of telephone exchange, that is the brain. In such a nerve-muscle system with a central control office it is possible to move the muscles in the proper sequence and have them contract to the proper degree so that some sensible act can be performed.

If one looks at the nervous system of various invertebrate organisms, one can find impressive trends in increase in complexity of the brain, and these trends are present and distinct, as well, among vertebrates all the way up to man. This in fact is why we think of man at the upper end of the scale and why in general we are so pleased with ourselves. On the lower end of the scale the hydroids (*e.g., Hydra*) and jellyfish are interesting, because they have no brain center but simply a continuous web of nerves, a nerve net. The result is that if there is a contraction or a stimulus at one point, this stimulus will pass as a wave around the animal. To emphasize this point there is the old experiment of A. Mayer, who cut the center of a jellyfish out with a cookie cutter so that a ring, a doughnut, was left; by stimulating at a point and damping out the stimulus going in one direction with a lump of ice, he caused the other stimulus to go around and around unimpeded for many hours until the ring died. Besides nerve and muscle a system of co-ordination depends upon receptors, organs that are specially adapted to respond to external stimuli. The eye responds to light with the wonderful result of vision; the ear responds to sounds; chemicals are recorded by taste and smell organs of different kinds; and there are various structures in the skin and in balancing organs that respond to mechanical pressure or touch. To say that the nervous system is a stimulus-response system is so obvious that it hardly needs saying.

Co-ordination, besides being mediated by nerve impulses, is also mediated by hormones, as we saw for plants. Animals too have elaborate hormone systems, some of which have been mentioned. In this case the chemical messages are carried by the blood circulation. Again there is a stimulus that leads to the production of a hormone, and one or more parts of the body respond specifically to the appearance of the hormone.

During the course of this discussion of mechanisms of feeding, reproduction, and co-ordination, as well as in the discussion of plant and animal evolution, we have been repeatedly confronted with two facts. By and large there has been an increase in size of animals, and there also has been an increase in complexity. We are now in a position to ask whether or not there is any connection between the two. Is it possible to become large without becoming complex? The answer, as we shall see, is definitely no and the reason pleasantly straightforward.

The reason is found in the principle of magnitude and the division of labor. The first step in its understanding involves a bit of geometry. Let us examine two balls, a golf ball and a basketball. In terms of the surface area (which is determined by $S = 4\pi r^2$) the basketball is clearly larger than the golf ball. In terms of volume the difference is even greater ($V = \frac{4}{3}\pi r^3$), for while the surface goes up as the square of the radius, the volume goes up as the cube. This can be stated in terms of a volume/surface ratio:

$$\frac{V}{S} = \frac{\frac{4}{3}\pi r^2}{4\pi r^3} = \frac{1}{3}r$$

This means that the larger the ball, the greater the volume as compared to the surface.

If we transfer from golf and basketballs to animals and plants, we see that there are certain living functions that depend on surfaces, such as gas exchange and food assimilation, while there are other functions that depend upon volume, such as combustion, metabolism, for after all, every cell metabolizes. Consider two hypothetical spherical organisms—one with a radius of a millimeter and the other with a radius of an inch. In the small one all the products of combustion and the gases and fuel necessary for combustion can easily reach the center of the mass by diffusion. However, in the case of the larger organism the center is far too remote from the surface for these exchanges to take place. In this particular case there would be two possible solutions. The surface could become folded and crinkled so that the ratio of surface to volume is kept the same as in the small organism. In this way, by the surface indentations, all interior parts would be near the surface, and foldings of this sort are found in gas-exchange structures, such as the gills and in food-assimilation structures, such as the small intestine, which is covered with the projecting, surface-increasing villi. The second method would be to have some sort of transport system to move the gases and the food, and this is found in the vascular systems of plants and animals. The same kind of argument can be brought forth for physical support, because strength is a function of the radius squared, but weight is equivalent to volume and a function of the weight cubed.

From this one can see that if there is a selection pressure for size increase, there must also be a selection pressure for an increase in complexity. Size increase alone would be impossible. On the other hand, it is possible to have an increase in complexity without an increase in size; the dependency is a one-way proposition. Therefore, one can have a decrease in size, and the complexity may not alter; such is certainly the case in many small animals—for example, in hummingbirds and shrews.

There is another interesting aspect to the relation of complexity to size increase that has been emphasized by B. Rensch. If one has a steady selection for size increase (as, for instance, in the evolution of the horse), then there must have been a corresponding increase in the size of the brain (Figure 19). The result should be greater intelligence, greater learning ability, greater ability to

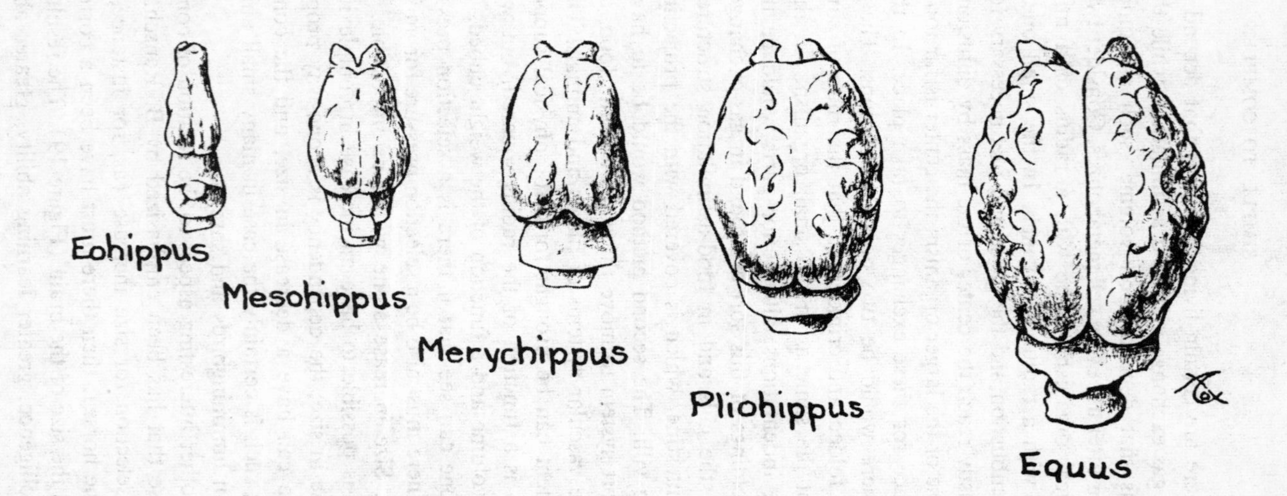

Fig. 19 Increase in the brain size of horses. (After T. Edinger.)

cope with the environment in a flexible fashion. These advantages could theoretically be so considerable that they themselves might be in part responsible for the selection pressure for increased size. To support his argument Rensch has performed learning tests on closely related animals of different sizes that seem to support his hypothesis, and he has even suggested that this is why the elephant never forgets. The importance of brain size as a factor in evolution is perhaps still problematical, although these ideas are, indeed, stimulating and to the point.

Thus far the prime emphasis has been on size and its effect on complexity in the consideration of these twin properties. Turning to the problem of complexity itself, let us first consider the oft-repeated evolutionary step from a single-celled to a multicellular organism. In the single cell we have one unit that performs all the functions, and the labor is divided within it. Even in the most primitive multicellular organisms we find some division of labor, and some cells become specialized in their function. For example, in the lowly sponges there are flagellated cells (collar cells) that both move the water and remove the food particles from the flowing stream; and there are surface covering cells, contractile cells around some of the canal openings, and finally wandering amoebae of various sorts, some of which specialize in the manufacturing of skeletal spicules. Put in another way this means that originally a multicellular organism was a collection of unicellular organisms that were physically attached, but eventually, through selection and the need of improved efficiency of function, the division of labor became marked so that the individual cells were no longer separate organisms but part of a new, larger, and more complex organism. If one were to examine cell colonies that exist today among the algae, the protozoa, and other aberrant groups, one would find every intergradation from groups of individual unicellular organisms that seem accidentally stuck together to well-integrated yet primitive multicellular organisms. This kind of observation leads to the old question of what is an individual, and the answer seems to be that there is no sharp division line when a group of cell individuals merge to form a true multicellular individual; there is a continuum between the two extremes.

If this be the case with unicellular organisms, why would it not be possible for multicellular organisms to be attached and form a sort of superorganism? If there really is no sharp division line between levels, it should be possible to do at least a double compounding. There are, of course, excellent examples of this among many plants and divers groups of invertebrates, but the most striking case is that of the colonial hydroids, which will serve as excellent representative examples (Figure 20).

In the case of the familiar *Hydra* there is a single polyp—that is, a mouth surrounded by a ring of tentacles and a body that amounts to no more than a tubelike gut cavity. There is excellent evidence that *Hydra* is not a primitive form but a degenerate colonial hydroid. From the recent work of P. Brien we know that the tentacle end of *Hydra* has a growth zone that is continually adding new tissue and causing elongation, while at the posterior end there is a constant destruction of cells. Since the production and destruction are roughly equal, there is never any significant elongation of a mature individual.

By contrast, the more primitive colonial hydroids, such as *Obelia,* grow at one end, but there is no cell degeneration at the other. In this way the gut stalks may become increasingly longer. Furthermore, they branch, and at the ends of each branch a new polyp develops. This is the reason that they are called colonial, for each *Hyrda*-like polyp is connected through the branching gut system to all the others in the colony; it is like all the bathrooms in an apartment house being connected by their plumbing.

In some of the species known today all the polyps have the same function. They all are capable of feeding, of catching food and pushing it into their mouths, and they all are capable of sprouting small reproductive bodies. In *Obelia* and related species, however, there is a radical change. While the majority of the polyps retains its ability to feed, a few lose it and become entirely devoted to the function of reproduction. They "bud off" small medusae in various stages of development, and these medusae produce the egg and sperm that after fertilization give birth to a new colony. It is fortunate that these reproductive polyps, which are incapable of feeding, are connected through their gut system

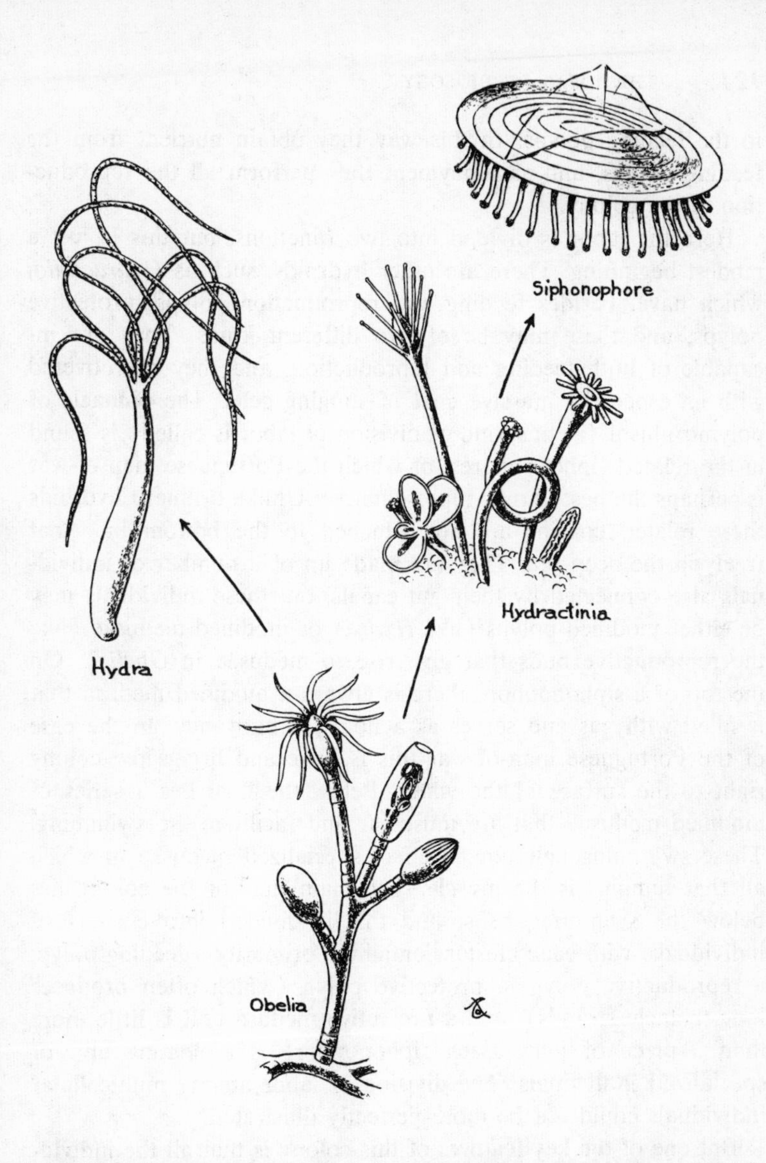

Fig. 20 Compound multicellular organisms among the colonial hydroids. The only form that can be considered a single individual is the degenerate *Hydra*. The others are made up of two or more different kinds of individuals or polyps which specifically serve the functions of feeding, reproduction, or protection.

to the feeding polyps. In this way they obtain nutrient from the feeding polyps, and as repayment they perform all the reproduction of the colony.

Here the labor is divided into two functions, but this is just a modest beginning. There are other hydroids, such as *Hydractinia,* which have, besides feeding and reproduction polyps, protective polyps, and these may be of two different kinds. They are incapable of both feeding and reproduction, and they are covered with an especially massive coat of stinging cells. The pinnacle of polymorphism (as this kind of division of labor is called) is found in the related siphonophores, of which the Portuguese man-of-war is perhaps the best known representative. Unlike ordinary hydroids these related cousins are not attached to the bottom but float freely in the deep sea. They are made up of a number of individuals also connected by their gut canals, but these individuals may be either modified polyps (like *Hydra*) or modified medusae (like the reproductive buds that give rise to medusae in *Obelia*). On the top of a siphonophore there is always a modified medusa that is filled with gas and serves as a float for buoyancy. In the case of the Portuguese man-of-war this is huge and brings the colony right to the surface of the water. Below the float lies a series of modified medusae that are muscular and facilitate the swimming. These swimming bells are in effect specialized medusae in which all that remains is the muscle. The main part of the colony lies below the swimming bells, and this is divided into clusters of individuals, with each cluster containing primarily a feeding polyp, a reproductive polyp, a protective polyp (which often produces long tentacle strands), and a protective medusa that is little more than a piece of jelly. Each siphonophore is a floating unit of specialized individuals. The division of labor among multicellular individuals could not be more perfectly illustrated.

But one of the key features of this colony is that all the individuals are attached. In fact they all came from the same fertilized egg and never separated. This is a kind of integration of numerous multicellular organisms in which the individuals are physically bound to one another. This means that they may (in fact *must*) have a continuous gut system, and they have a continuous nerve net. The problem of co-ordinating the individuals into one superunit, therefore, becomes simple. The stimulus-and-response systems within the whole colony can easily operate within the continuous mass so the divided labor can act in concert.

To have this kind of co-ordination, even with a division of labor, it is not necessary to have the animals physically attached to one another. When separation occurs, we no longer refer to the group as a colony but as a society. By a stretch of the imagination it might be possible to consider some groups of closely associated plants a society, but the word takes on greater significance with animal groups.

By social we simply mean that there is an interaction between individuals. According to this definition, most invertebrates and all vertebrates are social, for mating alone would certainly be a social act. There is, however, a great spectrum of degrees of being social, and some animals, as we shall see, have most elaborate societies.

The interaction between individuals that are not physically attached can occur in many ways. They involve the transfer of signals, and these signals can be chemical, visual, auditory, or even mechanical. This means that the animals must have the power to emit signals, such as an odor, a display or posture of some sort, a sound, a cry, or a push. Just as important is the reception of the signal by the other animal or animals in the group, and for this there are the special receptors of the nervous system, such as the chemical receptors that record odors, the eyes that record visual images, the ears that record sound, and the pressure-touch receptors that record contact. In some of the more primitive invertebrates these receptors may be very rudimentary, but they, nevertheless, can serve effectively in this social communication.

It is vitally important at this juncture to show that from a functional point of view there is no difference between the kind of communication we are discussing here—between separate individuals and the type of communication that occurs within a colonial siphonophore, and the type of communication that occurs within a mass of cells, such as in the developing embryo or the functional multicellular organism. In each case there are stimulus-reponse systems that are mediated by signals, and all these systems are characterized by two basic features. They occur in steps in which one stimulus-response reaction leads to the next, and they automatically integrate all the parts (be they cells, tissues, attached or separate organisms) into a co-ordinated whole.

Since this communication system in animal societies is largely dependent upon or made possible by the nervous system, it will be useful to consider some of the recent work of the ethologists K. Lorenz, N. Tinbergen, and others. They have been particularily concerned with the mechanics of behavioral stimulus-response systems. By means of studies both of animals in nature and of the same animals in the laboratory, they have shown that an animal will have under particular circumstances a response that it is prepared to elicit. If the stimulus is purposely not provided, then the desire to respond is frustrated, and the disturbance created by this frustration will be seen in some form of spontaneous energy outlet. If, on the other hand, the suitable stimulus is provided, then the distinctive response fires off like a loaded gun. It is even possible to analyze by experiment what aspect of the stimulus is especially effective.

To give some examples: when a herring-gull chick is approached by its mother, the chick pecks at the mother's bill, and the mother responds by regurgitating an appetizing dead fish. The chick responds only to a bill-like structure, and the mother gives its regurgitation response only when a chick pecks at it. We plainly see the stepwise nature of these stimuli and responses. In an attempt to find what aspect of the mother acted as a stimulus to the chick to peck in the first place, Tinbergen made cardboard models of the head and bill of an adult herring gull. He found that a certain over-all shape similar to the mother's was necessary and that the spot on the bill was especially stimulating. Even its color was important, and red (which is the natural color) was more effective than any other in eliciting the response.

Another similar experiment was done with the effect of egg shape, egg size, and egg color on the brooding response in herring gulls. Again a variety of wooden blocks of all different shapes (even a square egg) and colors were tried. The most significant conclusion from this study was the fact that the largest egg gave the most vigorous response, and Tinbergen reports a case of a small oyster catcher trying desperately to stay on top of a huge herring-gull egg. The most effective stimulus is, therefore, not one ordinarily encountered by the bird, and this serves to emphasize how a response can be tailored to a specific stimulus.

The stepwise nature of these stimulus-response systems is beautifully illustrated in the courtship process as seen, for example, in Tinbergen's work on the small, fresh-water, three-spined stickleback. (Figure 21). In this species the male builds a small nest out of algae and guards a territory around the nest. The females swim by in schools, and as they approach the territory of the male, he will make a zigzag dance toward a female. If she is at the right point in her sexual cycle and receptive, she will respond by showing the red underside of the belly. (If she is not ready she will flee.) The male responds to this signal by leading off to the nest and points to it with his snout. She responds by entering the nest; he in turn responds by poking her above her tail region with his snout, and she responds by egg-laying. The fact that these are sequential steps and that each step is dependent upon the existence of the previous one has been demonstrated by a whole series of experiments, many of which involve wooden models of one of the courting fish. Everything indicates that the female will not lay unless she is poked by the male; and the male will not poke unless the female has entered the nest, and she will not enter the nest unless he noses it with his snout—and so forth right to the beginning. If during normal courtship one step is missing, then the whole process stops. This is exactly what happens when closely related species attempt to mate and when one species has a slight modification of one of the steps; this brings an immediate halt to the mating and prevents hybridization between the two species.

From what has been said about these stimulus-response systems that operate between social animals it is evident that communication between individuals is important in a number of different processes in their life cycle. In mating we have just seen one example from the great multitude that could be provided. The function of this elaborate communication seems to be to provide the simul-

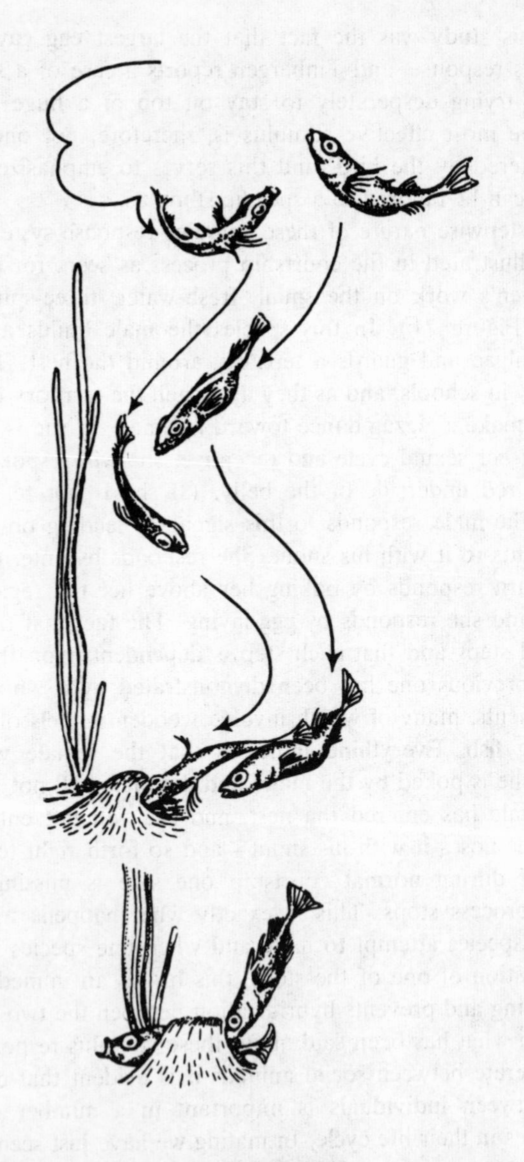

Fig. 21 The courtship of the three-spined stickleback. The male is on the left and the female on the right. (From N. Tinbergen.)

taneous shedding or coming together of egg and sperm at the moment they are both ripe and to insure in some cases that the male and female gametes are from the same species. It is significant that there is what amounts to a double check in order that these functions should be properly fulfilled. One, which we are presently discussing, is on the level of behavior, and the other is on the chemical level and concerns the chemical cross reactions between egg and sperm as they approach one another in the fertilization process. Here also it will be remembered there is a series of steps, one dependent upon the other, and the steps also have specific stimuli and responses although they are chemical rather than behavioral. Even hybrid prevention can and does often occur on this chemical level by slightly altering one of the steps. In having two separate systems that perform the same function there is that much more assurance that all will run smoothly and that there will be that many more permutations of possible change by selection for evolutionary progress.

Continuing along with the life history: development follows fertilization, and we have seen in some detail to what extent this is a sequential, stepwise process. After birth there is a period of parental care in many vertebrates (at least, birds and mammals), and again we see a social interaction between two individuals, in this case between parent and child. We saw, with food-begging in the herring-gull chick, an instance of a stepwise stimulus-response system, but, of course, there are many others for this species alone. That many of the steps are specific is indicated by the fact that in birds or mammals whose young are herded together in one large nursery or crèche (*e.g.*, penguins or seals) any mother will be able to pick out her own child from the multitude. Also it is important to remember that behavior activities are dependent upon internal physiological conditions of the individual. Hormones in particular are important in this regard, and the presence of various sex hormones are essential for courtship, as well as all aspects of parental care, and certainly the growth changes of the offspring are accompanied by large changes in their behavioral activity. The external stimulus-response systems are always dependent upon internal ones.

The most significant point from all this is that, over and above our previous conclusion that the whole life history in all its phases involves internal stepwise stimulus-response systems, we can now say that in social animals all stages of their life history, except those that occur in the isolation of an egg case, a uterus, or a pupal case, have clear-cut, external stepwise stimulus-response systems.

Let us briefly examine some elaborately social organisms, for the examples presented thus far represent average rather than extreme cases. The most striking of all animal societies are to be found among the insects. These remarkably abundant organisms have lived successfully in every conceivable ecological niche for many millions of years. Among their many exploits in adaptation, they have upon a number of separate, independent occasions developed some kind of social system. The most striking systems are found among the termites, the ants, and the bees, and in one glance at each of these groups we must again look sharply at the extent and the kind of communication system.

The study of termite societies has been especially rewarding in that it has demonstrated the existence of social hormones, chemical substances that can be passed from one individual to another and that control the pattern of the whole society. In all these insect societies the colony is started by one pair. In termites the king persists, and the queen is repeatedly fertilized by him. The eggs develop directly into small nymphs that undergo a series of molts, and often they never mature but stay perpetually adolescent and continue to molt periodically. These nymphs are the labor force (termites have no child labor laws). They may become mature, however, and molt either into an armored soldier or into a secondary reproductive, that is, a sort of substitute king or queen (Figure 22).

Each colony has only one king and one queen and a fixed proportion of soldiers. If these are eliminated in some catastrophe, after a few molts the proper proportion is restored. There is a division of labor within the society, and this division is made in a fixed proportion, exactly as is true of embryonic development. From the work of S. F. Light and M. Lüscher the evidence is excellent that the king and queen are constantly giving off substances that inhibit the molting nymphs from developing into reproductives. But if the king and queen are eliminated, so is the chemical inhibition, and at the next molt new secondary reproductives appear. This chemical is passed from the queen and spreads to all the nymphs by the constant licking of one another. By this method it is possible to rapidly spread a chemical signal throughout the colony. The same method is thought to apply to the control of the

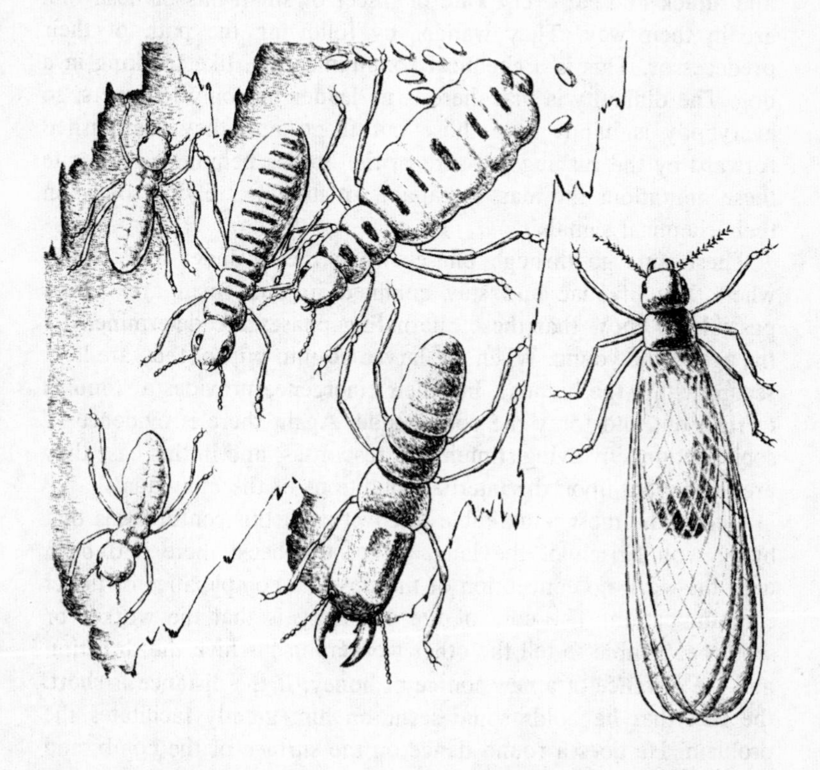

Fig. 22 Different types of termites showing various castes. On the left are three nymphs or workers. An egg-laying queen is shown above, and a virgin winged queen of another species is shown on the right. The individual in the middle is a soldier with large mandibles.

soldiers. It also should be added that the communication system is no doubt more complex than this, as recent studies seem to indicate; but the basic principle remains sound.

Communication in ant societies is not so well understood even though the variety of societies available for experimental material is great. Army ants are the exception, as shown by the work of T. C. Schneirla on their behavior. These ants have atrophied eyes and are blind, yet they can effectively wander out in large hordes and attack and eat every kind of insect or small bits of flesh that are in their way. They wander by following the path of their predecessor. This is a chemical communication, like tracking in a dog. The difficulty is that there is no leader but only followers, so everybody is happy save those out front, and they are pushed forward by the rushing pressure of the hordes behind. Yet despite these limitations the mass is capable of hunting, relying solely on their chemical signals.

These ants go through phases when they wander and phases when they bivouac and stay confined in one small area. It is possible to show that these alternating phases are determined by the age of the young. When the larvae go into pupae, they are kept secure within the bivouac, but their emergence provides a stimulus to rush out and foray the countryside. Again there is evidence of social actions involving stimuli and responses, and in this case they are dependent upon the internal conditions of the individuals.

One of the most remarkable discoveries of this century was that by K. von Frisch of the language of the bees; there had been until his work no conception of the possible complexities of insect communication. The core of the discovery is that the worker or scout bee is able to tell the other workers in his hive the direction and the distance of a new source of honey. If the distance is short, the fact that he holds some scent on him greatly facilitates the problem. He does a round dance on the surface of the comb, and this dance means look about near the hive; the scent gives a key to what to look for. If the new food is some distance, then the bee performs a figure-eight wagging dance in which the crossbar of the eight gives a key to the direction, and the rate at which the dance is performed indicates the distance. Rapid figure eights, with energetic wagging, mean a close distance (although farther out than the round-dance zone), and a slow wagging dance means a greater distance; it is even possible to plot a curve showing this inverse relation between dance rate and food distance. With these keys, von Frisch could guess himself where the new nectar source was located. One further remark should be made about direction. The sun is used as a guide, and the angle with the sun from the hive to the food is indicated by the straight part of the dance. When the sun is not visible, the bees can determine its position by the polarization of the light in the blue sky.

The complexity of these signals is truly amazing. Besides giving us a perfect example of social communications, it shows us (as was true also of the observations on army ants) that this communication may be instrumental in the communal food-gathering. Therefore, besides reproduction and its attendant parental care, feeding can be a living function that is carried out sometimes with an elaborate external communication system.

To make a switch to higher forms, there are many excellent studies on the social organization of birds and mammals. In these cases the prime bond is reproduction, for this is the phase of the life history that brings the animals together. It is not just the courtship and mating itself but many other aspects, such as child-rearing. For instance, in the rutting season in deer of all sorts, in horses, and in many similar animals there is a harem in which one dominant male brings together as many females as possible; by constant herding he attempts to keep them within his domain.

Another striking example of the importance of reproduction on social existence comes from the Alaskan fur seal which has extensive harems sometimes of more than a hundred cows. During this period the bull does not feed but keeps his cows safe from marauding bulls day and night. Therefore, the two short summer months are devoted entirely to reproduction, and the bulls can do their eating and fattening up during the rest of the year. (This reproductive period is so strenuous that they lose 200 pounds in one summer.) The reason for this is that the seal is an aquatic animal except for its reproduction, which must be on land. All year it spends virtually a solitary existence, but it concentrates its reproduction during the short temperate season of the Northern seal islands. To insure that this works out properly, the female has a special mechanism whereby pregnancy lasts very close to 365 days and fertilization can follow immediately after childbirth; everything has to happen in one short time in an intense, reproduction-oriented social season.

More examples of similar social periods of reproductive activity are easy to find, but, turning to other types of social activity, there are a number of ways in which animal grouping is significant in feeding or in insuring greater protection of the individuals. In deer (out of rutting season) the hinds will form small groups, and these have a leader, a dominant female. In some fine observations of F. F. Darling it was found that, if frightened, a group of hinds and their calves will form into a spindle-shaped group, with the leader at the tip and the second in command bringing up the rear. If they pass into a gully and disappear from sight, the second leader will fix the enemy with her intent gaze until the whole group has come up the other side. She will not lose sight of the potential danger until she sees that the leader has a fix on the same object, and then she catches up and joins the group.

The most obvious and common type of social communication connected with protection is the warning note. The hinds, for instance, when they first see danger, utter a warning bark. Since the leader is generally more watchful than the others, she will be the one to sound the alarm. Alarm notes among birds are particularly familiar to us, and, for instance, the rapid sharp cawing of a startled crow is not just to intimidate the intruder but to make his presence known to the other crows. Anticipating a subject that will be discussed presently, a particularly interesting aspect of alarm notes is that in any one community, many animals come to rely on the alarm notes of one species that is particularly observant; the cawing of one crow may not be just a signal for crows but for many other species as well. Another example is in the case of the fur seals, which completely lack an alarm signal and rely entirely upon the screaming of the gulls to herald danger.

Group feeding is another common form of social activity. A most striking case of this is found in wolves that hunt in packs.

Their tactics of running down prey and particularly their organized flanking movements involve a high degree of co-ordination between individuals. It is a well-defined, co-operative group effort.

A final example of grouping that is evident to some degree in the wolves and to an even higher degree in monkey societies is the family unit. The wolf pack is a relatively permanent cohesive group and not just a temporary arrangement for hunting. It usually centers around one dominant male and his female, although there will also be offspring and even grown individuals associated with the central couple. It is apparently extremely difficult for a lone wolf to join such a pack. He or she is, generally, attacked and repeatedly rebuffed. Even though it belongs to the same species, the newcomer is a foreigner. Baboons have similar family groups although these smaller groups may be within a larger troop of monkeys. A dominant male may have more than one wife, many offspring, and some associated bachelor males, whose presence is tolerated—but pity for them if they should show any signs of interest in the females in heat. All the activities of these subordinate males, even eating, must follow the master. And these as well as many other facets of their social existence are communicated to one another by gestures, postures, and noises, all part of their own special language.

So far in our discussion of superorganisms we have started within an individual and described how there is a communication between parts. Then we saw whole organisms attached together and ultimately divided in their labor in the colonial hydroids and siphonophores. Finally we have considered the case of unattached or social groups in which the separate individuals are bound together by a communication system and where there may even be a division of labor as seen in the castes of insect societies. It is now the moment to discuss those cases where there have been communication, co-ordination between two different species, and again here we will find that there are cases in which the two species are physically bound to one another (parasitism and symbiosis) and that there are others where the association is on the social or unattached level.

It is difficult to discuss parasitism and symbiosis separately, for there is no sharp division line between them. In both cases two organisms are living in physical contact with one another, and in parasitism the gain is presumed to be entirely on the side of the parasite while the loss is on the side of the host. In symbiosis both partners are presumed to gain, but it is often difficult, in fact rarely possible, to be certain what are gains and what are losses without knowing all the physiological and metabolic details of both individuals. The only clear-cut cases are those in which the partner kills the other outright; in this case, at least, the victor can make claim to more gains than the dead host, and we may confidently call this Pyrrhic victory parasitism.

In these close associations between individuals of separate species the association may remain throughout the whole life cycle. For instance, in the green *Hydra* there are small green algae in the cells, and these are passed on from generation to generation either through the asexual buds or through the eggs. There are other cases in which a coming together is required each new generation, and there can be special mechanisms to assure this reunion. For instance, the eggs of certain flatworms will attract their flagellated algal partners by giving off a chemical substance.

Associations of various sorts are exceedingly common. There are a huge number of invertebrates that harbor algae as in the two examples just mentioned. Besides algae, many animals live in conjunction with bacteria and filamentous fungi. Among mammals, for example, there is a large growth of bacteria in the gut that aids in the processing of food. This is particularly significant in the case of herbivores in which cellulose-degrading bacteria are used to help liberate the sugar from this stubborn food. All the bacterial and fungal diseases of animals and man are less happy examples of the same thing.

Animals live together with other animals, and protozoa also play a part as digestive aids in intestinal tracts. Besides mammals a striking example of this is found in the wood-eating termites, which have a species-specific protozoon in the anal end of their gut that performs the cellulose digestion. Each time the nymph molts it loses its pet protozoon in the old shell, but since, as we saw previously, they are constantly licking one another, they soon reinfect themselves. Other examples that could be mentioned are the many elaborate worm parasites of both vertebrates and invertebrates—the flukes, the tapeworms, the hookworms, etc.

If we turn to the plants, there are some examples of higher plants existing in conjunction with animals—such as nematode infestations of trees and crop plants. Were one to thumb through a book on plant pathology, one would be impressed by the variety of plant diseases, and the parasites are usually other plants, bacteria, and especially fungi.

There is also a whole group of organisms, the lichens, which consist of two plants living in what appears to be balanced harmony. These hardy crustlike double organisms cover rocks and trees especially in the unfavorable climates of the North. Their principle bulk is fungal, for the main structure is made up of a mass of their filaments; but within the mass, algal cells will be found clasped firmly in the fungal filaments (Figure 23). The presumption is that the algae provide photosynthetic products for the fungus and that the fungus provides housing and, possibly, nitrogenous materials for the algae. In any event they both live in stability. Their reproduction usually consists of balls of fungal cells surrounding some algae being carried to distant places by the wind; in other words they develop together, as well as live together. In the laboratory it is easy to separate the fungus from the alga and to grow them separately on prepared media; but the curious thing is that so far it has been impossible to persuade the separate plants to come back together after living for some time in isolation.

These dual organisms exist and develop, as do single organisms, by the communication of parts. The only difference here is that the parts may be from different species. The communication systems must be essentially the same, and one expects that an exchange of substances in what we previously called chemical conversation is the factor that allows them to grow together in specific steps and to function together in close harmony. In terms of communication systems the fact that there are two species involved instead of one seems to make little difference.

There can also be social relations between organisms of separate

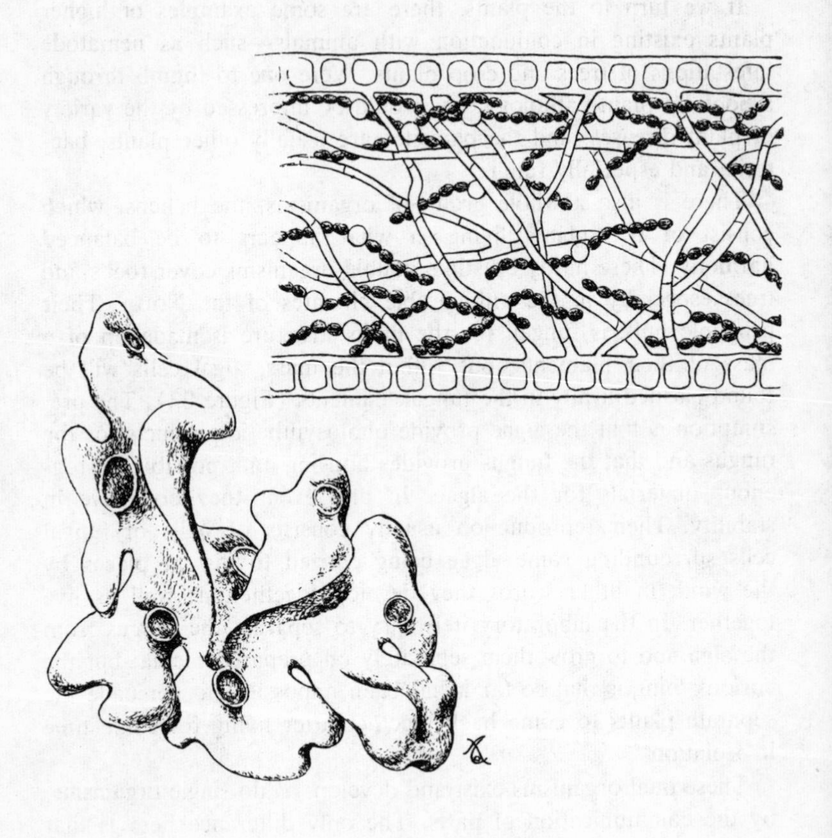

Fig. 23 A lichen. Below is the general structure of the plant and above is a microscopic cross section to show that among the fungal filaments there are chains of pigmented algal cells. (After B. Fink.)

species, although as before these communication systems at a distance are more common in animals. In the case of plants some species will give off substances that diffuse through the ground and prevent other species from growing in the near vicinity. (These substances also may serve to keep members of its own species at a healthy distance.) The antibiotics given off by fungi and other plants are cases in point. Among animals we have already mentioned an example of the alarm note of one species being useful to many others.

Parasitism can even take place without a physical binding between parasite and host. Such social parasitism occurs in the case of the European cuckoo, which lays its eggs in the nest of some other species. Because the young cuckoo chick gapes for food with such vigor and flamboyance, the foster mother neglects her own meek offspring. This is a case of the stimulus, the gape, eliciting a stronger response as performed by the parasite. The parasite is successful by cleverly splicing into this behavioral stimulus-response system, thereby giving the shameless mother cuckoo a carefree life.

Other examples may be found in the parasites of social insects. Certain beetles or sometimes other species of ants will join the colony and benefit by free meals and free housing. In ant colonies, for instance, there are many kinds of two-species colonies, and sometimes one species of ant will attack the ant hill of another and carry off its workers to use as slaves. They may also make use of aphids as sources of plant juices and keep them protected and contented like cows.

But the real implications of the social relations or the relations at a distance only become evident when one considers the whole community of animals and plants in one locale. There are influences that spread far beyond one species influencing or being influenced by the behavior pattern of another or one species producing a chemical that in some way affects another. All these small specific interactions lead to the major interactions that make up a new kind of unit, the community.

There is a balance in nature even though the balance may be constantly fluctuating, constantly changing. The word balance may, therefore, be somewhat misleading, because the important point is that not only do individuals affect other individuals, but populations of one species affect populations of another. This becomes obvious when one thinks of a limiting factor, such as food supply. In the broadest terms, if plants are greatly reduced, the animal population will also become reduced since one is dependent upon the other. Some specific plant may become diseased and decrease. If this plant is the food source of a particular rodent, then the number of the rodent will decrease. This in turn might cause the reduction in numbers of a particular hawk that feeds on this rodent. The loss of the plant may allow an increase in another that lives on similar terrain, and the rodent that is supported by this new increase will in turn increase and possibly affect the numbers of some other predator. This example is crude and oversimplified but it does serve to show the interdependence of all organisms in nature. Communities are a mass of complicated communication systems between individuals and groups of individuals, and because of this, one cause may have a great multitude of effects.

Since there are so many elements in a community and especially since they are so loosely bound together, a community is not to be compared with an organism so far as its efficiency as a stable unit. An organism can live and remain the same despite extraordinary external changes; its ability to remain internally constant irrespective of its surroundings is one of the wonders of the living world. But a whole community shifts and changes with the slightest climatic or even internal change (such as the example just given). Think, for instance, of the innocent introduction of the rabbit in Australia followed by its incredibly vigorous growth and spread throughout the continent. The whole ecological community of Australia has been changed to some extent by the introduction of this one species.

But in the case of the individual we stressed the point that its stability was caused by selection; stability was equivalent to fitness. Why is this not the case for the ecological community? The answer lies in the fact that the community change is essential for the evolution of new and improved stable species. If the community were fixed and stable, then evolutionary progress would be foiled. So in the last step of our road towards more complex life we find that natural selection still calls all the shots. Just as in mutation and sexuality, selection perfected and maintained a variation-producing mechanism, so in the shifts and changes of communities selection has perfected and maintained a further way of keeping a larger kind of variation or flux to allow for evolutionary innovations. Each level of complexity from the single cell up has been produced by selection and then used as an instrument in further selection. The specific steps that follow one from another have steadily increased in number and in scope, but each step was mediated by mutation, recombination, and selection, so that there could be a change from a simple communication within parts of a cell, to communication with parts of a multicellular organism, to communication between organisms of the same or different species, leading finally to the gigantic interrelation of all life on the face of the earth.

CHAPTER 6

MAN

In the discussion thus far a survey of the important themes in biology has been spread out for our scrutiny, and before the image dims it may be of interest to see how these themes apply to man. This will not be a dissertation on anthropology or sociology but almost entirely on the biology of man. By this is meant that we shall attempt to see in what way man is similar to other living beings and in what way he differs; we will try to find the borders where biology ceases and the other sciences of man begin. To do this it will be useful to follow roughly the outline that has been used already in this book and to begin with a consideration of man's evolution, his heredity, his development or life history, and finally his ecology, that is, his relation to other men, to other animals and plants, and to his environment in general. No attempt will be made to discuss the multitude of pertinent points, but the particularly significant ideas will be stressed.

EVOLUTION

We are at the moment in a period of active research on the ancestry of man. Largely through the new discoveries of fossil men in Africa, there are now a number of primitive human and advanced primate fossils, and we are slowly beginning to obtain some picture of man's early morphology. Undoubtedly new pieces to this puzzle will continue to emerge, and we may expect better and better skull and bone series of man's ancestors.

In discussing animal and plant evolution, rather than reconstructing the past from fossils, we have looked at existing types to try to learn, at least, what kinds of permutations exist today. From the physical point of view there are a number of different races of man on the surface of the earth, but anatomically they are all modern; there are no people existing today that are living fossils in this sense.

If we turn to behavior patterns instead of anatomical patterns, then certain primitive tribes, such as the Australian or the African Bushman, do seem to be kinds of living fossils. But their primitive behavior is only a superficial difference, and if a Bushman were brought to New York at an early receptive age, and given a good education, he would be an American in his behavior patterns. The point, of course, is that we are dealing here with cultural differences and not biological differences, and the distinction between the two is vitally important as far as man is concerned.

By culture we mean behavior patterns, customs, information that is handed down from generation to generation by learning. This is in sharp contrast to biological behavior patterns, which are presumably gene controlled, therefore, inherited and instinctive. But like so many sharp distinctions, this one is in fact dull and there are all sorts of shades between the two. In the first place culture transmission depends upon the ability to learn, to retain, and this capacity is gene controlled and inherited. The reason we say that man is a cultured rather than an instinctive animal is that his capacity to learn is so great compared to any other animal, that what instincts he may have are obscured and forgotten. The important thing to examine then is what, if any, are the cultural characteristics of animals other than man and what are the instinctive reactions of man.

Among animals it is extremely difficult to devise rigorous experiments that distinguish between learned and inherited responses. The usual method is to isolate an animal at birth, so that it is completely separated from its mother and any other members of its species whose actions it might parrot. The result is that it is possible to find some things the animal is incapable of doing, and, therefore, they are presumably cultural. But from the examples it will be evident that the result is not quite so clear-cut.

Working with army ants, T. C. Schneirla separated some cocoons from a bivouac and allowed them to hatch in isolation. He found that their activities exactly paralleled those of their mates that were left with the horde of ants, but they were slower in developing and took a day longer to perform the instinctive actions. One would expect lowly insects to have most of their behavior patterns fixed and gene controlled, and, indeed, learning only helps to speed up matters a small degree.

A great deal of work has been done on bird song. Some birds, such as mockingbirds, myna birds, or parrots (if the croaking of parrots can be called song), are well known to be excellent mimics. They have inherited a high capacity to learn. Many other birds have a basic song pattern, but, with learning, it can undergo many minor modifications. This is an old story to the canary-fancier who teaches the young birds by putting them near an old bird with a fine voice. (One can even buy Gramophone records of canary masterpieces to guide younger birds.) The same learning goes on in nature, and as a result different places will develop, through learning, different dialects. An extensive study of dialects in crow language from both America and Europe has been made; and even though the birds are the same species, by playing records of crows from one region to crows of another it is clear that the dialect is as meaningless as an English record might be to a French peasant. Here the basic pattern of noisemaking and the capacity to learn are inherited, and the rest is clearly cultural.

A final example of culture in animals is to be seen in an interesting experiment on chimpanzees performed at the Yerkes Laboratory in Orange Park, Florida. When the buildings were first constructed, they had a centrally located drinking fountain, a bubbler that needed to have the handle turned for the water to spout. In the beginning one ape was shown how this instrument worked, and since that moment some years ago, great care has been taken to prevent any other chimpanzee from seeing a human being operate a bubbler. Yet to this day, after numerous generations, all the colony can drink from a bubbler. This act has clearly been perpetuated by cultural tradition, for surely no chimpanzee from the African jungle would have inherited an instinct to operate a man-made drinking fountain.

Turning to the other side of the problem, if we look at man for evidences of instinctive actions, the problem of making any clear distinction or isolation of such actions becomes even more difficult. The one great characteristic of the evolution of man has been increase in brain size and his enormously enlarged capacity to learn; and what and how he learns is so omnipresent that to prove that any small action might be instinctive is often difficult or impossible. To make matters worse, this is a subject of changing fads and fancies. Fifty years ago the word instinct was acceptable, twenty years ago it was considered meaningless, and now it has regained favor. Fifty years ago there was a raging controversy, concerning the same point we are discussing here, as to whether nature or nurture made a greater contribution to an individual human being. By nature was meant his inheritance and by nurture his cultural environment. The supporters of nature would argue that certain families are noted for many generations of productive and exceptional individuals. Francis Galton was an originator of this idea over a hundred years ago, and, indeed, his own family was used as evidence. The Jukes and the Kallikaks, so prominent in all textbooks of biology and psychology just a few years ago, were pedigreed families of generation after generation of criminals and delinquents of the most sordid variety. The supporters of nurture pointed to Mogli and other wolf children and to the wild boy of Aveyron to show that if a child was isolated and raised in a separate environment it would take on wholly nonhuman characters (Romulus and Remus seem to be exceptions).

Today we would consider both of these extremes and particularly the examples as nonsense. The sociologists are quick to point out the fact that Galton's family maintained cultural traditions for a series of generations that were somewhat different from the murder, larceny, and rape of the Jukes and the Kallikaks; how any valid conclusion can be made from this on nature and nurture is hard to imagine. The wild boy of Aveyron and other so-called feral children have been shown, with the help of some mildly critical examination, to be cases of mentally deranged children, and the gazelles, the wolves, and the other motherly animals seem to have faded away.

About the best that can be done at the moment is to say that many reactions to particular situations are instinctive and innate. Fear, anger, joy, and all the basic emotions would fit in this category, although the stimuli that might elicit these reactions can certainly be modified to some extent by culture. Presumably the reactions of infancy and early childhood are especially likely to be innate, because they have not yet been buried by learned reactions.

We also know (as have dog breeders for hundreds of years) that certain general mental characteristics are inherited. It is possible to breed dogs for viciousness or docility or for retrieving, pointing, chasing, and all the other pursuits of working dogs. Another fine example may be found in sheep-breeding. Merino sheep always flock while Highland sheep spread. The reason is that in Spain the summer feeding and winter feeding of the sheep were widely separated, and the shepherd had to march them many miles along the road and through the villages. If they did not flock, they would soon be lost in their seasonal journey. On the other hand, the Scottish shepherd never moves his Highland sheep large distances and wishes them to spread out as much as possible over the hills so that no one area is overgrazed, and both of these characteristics have been achieved by selective breeding.

As far as man is concerned the difficulty is that nurture has become so tremendously important that nature is increasingly difficult to clearly identify and tag. But we know that some patterns of behavior of human beings must be wholly or at least in part instinctive. The only difficulty is that we are not entirely sure which ones and to what extent.

The increase in the importance of nurture or, better, the ability to learn in man has a tremendous consequence as far as his evolution is concerned. By passing information from father to son there is a new method of inheritance, and suddenly the human species is endowed with two extremely successful inheritance systems: a genetic one and a cultural one. Therefore, there can be a cultural evolution along with a biological evolution.

We know that in biological evolution, mutation, recombination, and selection are the means of change. Given an organism capable of extensive learning, cultural evolution works by an entirely different system. All that is needed is a new idea, an invention, and this new idea can be immediately accepted by a whole population and directly passed on to the entire next generation. Mutation and selection are haphazard processes usually involving only small steps at a time, and selection requires many generations for these steps to be evident to any degree in a population. In other words by comparison to biological evolution, cultural evolution is extremely rapid, and while it took perhaps a million years for man to evolve from the higher primates, we have come from the Stone Age to the atomic age in less than ten thousand years.

So many of the cultural changes are the result of the combined efforts of invention and that peculiar, ill-defined quality called style. Frequently the products of these twin instruments of change are left behind and give a kind of fossil record of their own. Architecture is a particularly good example, and we can, for instance, trace the changes from the Greek and Roman temples, to the early Christian Byzantine and Romanesque churches, up to and through the early and late Gothic cathedrals. The changes in this series are tremendous (especially if they be compared to the structural changes of a skeleton), yet they took only a few thousand years to occur while the skeletal change from fish to mammals took more than two hundred million years. The inventions in this architectural series came in the modification of the arch as a means of support and various other structural changes that permitted larger buildings, while the style transformation is seen in all the small detailed carvings and trimmings, as well as in some of the major lines.

In our sometimes desperate attempt to distinguish man from the animals two examples are usually given of inventions that mark us apart. One is fire, and, indeed, there are no other animals that can use fire, and this certainly is one of the greatest of man's inventions. The other is the use of tools, and in this man is not unique. We have already seen the case of the Galápagos finch, which fills the ecological niche of a woodpecker and to compensate for his lack of an appropriate long beak picks at the bark with the spine of a cactus. Another and even more fantastic example comes from those curious birds of Australia and neighboring islands called bowerbirds. Depending upon the species, the male builds some kind of structure, usually out of branches, that serves as a courtship rostrum. The construction is often elaborate, and about it will be placed different colored objects to give the effect of a garden. As a final touch some species will take a wad of vegetable matter in their bills and brush it against charcoal from some extinct brush fire and rub it on the inside sticks of the bower. Other species will do their interior decorating by rubbing the juice of a blueberry as a source of paint. The physiological function of all this activity apparently is merely an exceptionally elaborate courtship display, so elaborate that even a paintbrush is employed (Figure 24).

But in man it is not so much the fact that he uses tools that distinguishes him; it is the kind of tools. The spear, the bow and arrow, the wheel, the lever, and the development of suitable materials, such as metals, sparked the cultural changes of man. And as history proceeds we have one invention succeeding another until we come to our own age of extraordinary technology.

Another distinguishing feature of man is supposed to be language. As we learn more about communication in animals, we realize that the amount and kinds of information that can be exchanged by animals is far greater than was previously suspected. Even lowly bees can communicate distance and direction to their hive mates. Therefore, certainly, language in any sense is far from unique in man; again it is a matter of degree. The fact that man has developed a complex set of symbols and especially the fact that these can be easily recorded (writing being one of the important inventions of man) have certainly materially assisted in all the cultural changes we are discussing. Writing has left a beautifully detailed fossil record of our past history. And all the technology that we know today is only possible because of our efficient language communication system and all the physical aids

Fig. 24 Courtship of the satin bower bird. The male parades in front of the bower and just before copulation the female crouches in the central avenue. (Drawing by E. Mose in *Scientific American.*)

that help it, such as the telephone. Just as biological evolution depends on and improves an efficient communication system, so does cultural evolution.

Imagination is often cited as another unique property. This and other psychological attributes are often hard to evaluate and measure, but again it must be thought of in terms of degree. It is, nevertheless, striking in man that superstition is so widespread and manifest in so many ways even among the most civilized of people, and at the same time it is hard to see any equivalent phenomenon in animal behavior. It would seem to be a by-product of our more active and more complex brains.

As a last characteristic of man, let us consider free will. Man is supposed to be superior to all other forms of life because he is capable of making his own decisions. It is my view that this is a highly overrated distinction and again a matter of degree. Animals certainly do make decisions and do exert their free wills. The choice they have to make may not be very interesting, but they are constantly faced with two or more alternatives in their existence in nature, and they must and do choose. On the other side of the ledger, many decisions we make that we consider to be exercises of free will are in reality not completely so. We may even subconsciously be influenced by customs, by internal drives, by public opinion, and by many other factors that tend to erode the freedom of our wills. Our greater brain size has produced more possibilities for free and imaginative choices, but our greater brain size has permitted more complex forces to influence our choices.

In evolution man has come from primates, and in so doing he has not lost his genes, his flesh and blood, his animal nature. But he has been greatly improved in his ability to learn and to transmit information, and, therefore, the power of cultural evolution has opened up to him, and he has exploited it with zest and vigor. Alongside this novelty all other special properties of man seem pale by comparison. But each one, this one included, is a matter of degree. The increase in brain size and complexity produced an increase in ability to learn, to imagine, to decide, etc. In some cases the advance had little effect, but in others it was enough to open up new vistas, a new world—a world in which for the first time in the whole of life, natural selection is no longer the sole agent of change.

This brings us to the final topic of our discussion, for if cultural change has these profound effects, we may well ask: is selection affecting mankind in any way whatever? The answer is most definitely affirmative, for historical changes may affect the direction of selective forces, but they certainly cannot eliminate them. The real evidence for selection comes when it can be shown that different people from different geographic areas have different genes. If this is so, then we have *prima-facie* evidence that selection has occurred recently. Since the evidence is genetic, let us move on to the next subject.

GENETICS

The fact that there are human races is the evidence that there are different gene pools. The physical traits of Negro, Eskimo, or Indian are genetically determined and, therefore, arose by selection. For the most part we are in a state of the most profound ignorance of what are the selective advantages or disadvantages of any particular racial characteristics. It is always presumed, for instance, that the black skin is a particular adaptation to the African sun; but when the physiologist examines the situation closely, there does not seem to be any reason why a white man would not fare well in a similar climate, and in fact he does. The high cheek bones of the Eskimo and his body proportions are supposed to be climatic adaptations, but again no one can show that they are superior physiologically in the arctic environment. The answers may come with further study, but they must be discovered by physiological experiments, not by complacent speculation.

Better evidence for adaptation may be found in the curious case of the gene that is responsible for the disease called sickle-cell anemia. In the black population of Africa there is a high frequency of this gene. This is all the more puzzling because in the homozygous form (that is, both homologous genes are sickle cell) the individual has a peculiar form of hemoglobin that causes the red cells to adopt a sickle shape and usually results in the early death of the individual. One would expect that such an unfavorable gene would be rapidly selected out, yet to the contrary, it is prevalent. The explanation probably lies in the fact that the heterozygote (one sickle-cell gene and one normal gene) is especially resistant to a common and serious form of malaria found in many parts of Africa. Therefore, the selection pressure for the heterozygotes is so strong that the gene is retained in quantity even though its homozygote is lethal. If this explanation is correct, and there is no evidence to the contrary, then we have here a perfect example of selection operating upon a human population.

Generally it is more difficult to approach human population genetics problems than those of animals, because so few of the genes are known. One approach has been to compare the over-all genetic consequences of crossbreeding in large urban populations with inbreeding in small rural populations. The prediction that such inbreeding will unmask undesirable and desirable genes is found to be true, as it also is in many inbred royal lines.

One of the greatest changes for human population genetics is the increase in transportation and, therefore, the mass movement of peoples. The result is that today on the earth, instead of favoring geographic or other kinds of isolation, the whole world population has become a melting pot in which the racial differences are slowly being diluted. It is as though in the race formation of primitive prehistory man had been destined ultimately to become different species by geographic isolation, but with the mixing due to migration and travel the different peoples are being poured back into the pot. Does this mean that we are headed for a world in which there will eventually be complete genetic homogeneity? The answer is problematical, but if it occurs, it will also mean that by such standardization we will to a large extent be frustrating selection as an agent of change. Only those conditions that select for the whole world's human population will be effective, and any regional selection will be diluted immediately.

There has often been talk of eugenics, of breeding humans in such a way as to improve their gene pool—a kind of unnatural selection or self-domestication. While theoretically this is not an impossible approach, it is beset with two great difficulties: we know so little of human genes that what to select is uncertain, and the moral revulsion that comes with manipulating humans will be hard to overcome. This seemed a simpler proposition to the intellectuals of the 1920's than it does to us today.

Human genetics is in a very sad state compared to that of the fruit fly or the bread mold. A mere handful of genes are understood and known, such as the celebrated gene which causes hemophilia. In that royal disease, which is often fatal, the blood does not clot. Its special interest is that the gene is on one of the sex chromosomes (the X chromosome), of which the female has two and the male one. Therefore, if a man has one of these recessive genes (and he can have no more than one since he has only one X chromosome), he has the disease; but a woman will show no signs of the disease with one of the genes, for the other X chromosome will have a dominant normal gene. She, therefore, becomes a carrier unless she receives a hemophilia gene from both her parents, and then she, too, has the disease. But as in sickle-cell anemia, the chance of such a recessive homozygote is rare.

Many characters, for instance, hair and eye color, are usually governed by a number of genes. Generally brown eyes are dominant over blue, but the browns and the blues can be of such complex genetic make-up that the result is not always predictable.

One especially rewarding method of genetic analysis of human beings is the examination of identical twins. If the twins are identical, they come from the same fertilized egg (by an early doubling of one embryo), while fraternal twins come from two separate eggs fertilized by two separate sperm and, therefore, are entirely different genetically. In this way it is possible to study cases of identical twins who have been separated and to find how differences in environment might affect their natures and how much is genetic and, therefore, innate.

One of the difficulties that must be carefully examined in such experiments is to be certain that the twins really are identical and not just fraternal twins who closely resemble one another. Even a close correspondence of external morphology and performance in psychological tests may leave some lingering doubt. There is now a method that is considered most effective to prove that the twins are not identical, although it cannot positively prove the reverse. It is pertinent here, because it shows how sensitive a test must be to reveal gene differences.

If one is infected by the germ of some disease, there is a mechanism in our bodies whereby the cells in the lymph nodes build up a quantity of large protein molecules called antibodies. These antibodies are capable of reacting with the products of the germ (antigens), and in this way the germ is finally conquered, and good health returns. Should one be reinfected with the same germ later on, one does not again get the disease; it is immediately rejected by one's antibodies, which have remained from the previous bout. All inoculations and vaccinations are designed either to provide antibodies directly or to allow the body to make its own antibodies to particular diseases.

This discussion is by way of a preamble to the problems connected with skin grafting. If a person has a severe burn and the skin is lost over a large area, it is helpful to re-cover this area with skin, for the burn's scar tissue is rigid and inflexible. This can be done by carefully slicing the skin from some other area in two sheets, leaving the bottom sheet *in situ* and placing the top sheet over the raw region. Both will regenerate completely new skin in their respective areas. However, if the skin is taken from another person, it will grow and look healthly for a few weeks; but then, suddenly, it will turn black, die, and be sloughed off. The reason is that the donor of the skin graft had a different genetic constitution (he may be a fraternal twin), and the lymph glands of the host made antibodies that caused its destruction—as though it were a foreign germ. It cannot do this to its own skin, nor to the skin of an identical twin, because the genetic constitutions and, therefore, the antigenic constitution of both host and graft are identical.

This should mean that if two twins are tested by putting a skin graft of one upon the other and if the graft stays indefinitely, the twins are identical; but if it is rejected, they are fraternal twins. Because of an interesting new problem only the latter conclusion is possible; if the skin graft is kept, they still might be fraternal twins. P. B. Medawar and R. E. Billingham made the discovery that this can occur by the fact that the placental circulation of the two nonidentical twins are fused or connected and that there is an exchange of cells between the two embryos. In this way both fraternal twins will have lymph-node cells of the other as well as their own and, therefore, will tolerate both skins. They were able following this discovery to produce tolerant mice by injecting the lymph-node cells of one genetic strain of mice into the fetus of another. The implications of this important discovery are being pursued both in the practical problem of grafting surgery and in the more fundamental problem of development in general. To us in this discussion the interesting point is that it is possible either naturally (in fraternal twins with joint fetal circulation) or artificially to produce an individual with both the cells of its own genetic constitution and those of another individual. These chimeras or genetically composite individuals are found among human fraternal twins.

Besides anitigen-antibody reactions, there is another rather crude but interesting way to distinguish twins. Police dogs that are skilled in following scents cannot distinguish between identical twins; if one twin commits the crime, the identical brother is just as likely to be tracked down. The dogs can show some recognition of fraternal twins; that is, if they are confronted with two brothers among a group of otherwise unrelated people, they will pick them both out if given the scent of one beforehand. The process is far more hesitant, however, than when they are identical. The complex cell chemistry must produce extraordinarily subtle differences in odor, and each of these differences is gene controlled.

DEVELOPMENT

One of the most interesting aspects of human development is the fact that it is so slow as compared to other animals—that is, the length of time between fertilization and maturity is greatly extended. The fetal period itself is not unusually long, for large mammals, such as the hippopotamus, have a pregnancy of eight months and the elephant one of eighteen months. But in those huge beasts sexual maturity is reached long before it is in humans. If one looks to the great apes, a chimpanzee is sexually mature at the age of seven. This is intermediate between slow man and the rapid lower animals.

This longer period of growth has many interesting consequences. It means among other things a far more extended period of parental care. But more important, and this may be the key to the whole phenomenon, it provides a far more extended period of learning. During youth the brain is in a plastic, receptive condition, and by having a long time to learn and to establish memory pathways in the brain, it is possible ultimately to bring forth the fantastic complexity that is the human mind. Therefore, the long period of development to maturity may not be an idle one but one devoted to properly composing the nervous system.

There are a number of evidences that this longer period of growth and development has occurred by heterochrony. That is, genes which determine the rate of maturing have been altered by mutation and selection so that the embryonic and youthful periods are extended. The particular heterochrony is, therefore, neoteny, for neoteny is the prolongation of youthful characters into adult life. Besides the slow mental development, there is the fact that man is hairless, the condition equivalent to that of a fetal monkey. But there are a number of other features of grown men that are embryonic: the relatively large brain weight, the tooth arrangement, the flat face, and the curvature of the skull in relation to the spinal cord. Even the sutures of the skull close and seal off at a much later period than in monkeys or other mammals. From this impressive list one must conclude that the mental superiority of man has been achieved by the prolongation of youth. If a machine is to be more complex, it takes a longer time to put it together, and, therefore, a longer time of pliability is necessary for the construction. Also this emphasizes how much of man's character depends upon learning and how much the brain is molded by the environment, by parents, by school, and by all phases of experience. What is inherited is the capacity to learn, and this capacity is carefully exploited over an extended period.

Another interesting aspect in the development of man (which we are using here in the broader sense of life history) is the question of old age or senescence. More than with other animals we are aware of the fact that human beings get old; this means far more to us than an increase in years but a genuine running down of the human machine or what has been called an increase in decrepitude. The changes that take place as the machine wears out are possible to describe anatomically, but their cause is still mysterious. If certain tissues are removed from the body, they can maintain continuous and vigorous growth in culture tubes on artificial media for very long periods of time (perhaps indefinitely), but in the body these same tissues wear out in senility. To some extent it can be shown that the glands that produce hormones show signs of failing, and the failure in turn affects other tissues; yet the artificial addition of the hormones makes only small and transient improvements. And what produces the gland changes in the first place? The only thing we have strong reason to suspect is that the changes are gene controlled and that the decline of the body is determined by the hereditary make-up just as was its original building. We come back to our statement that all phases of the life history are periods of gene action and under genetic control.

Of course, this does not mean that genes determine the day we will die. Genes determine the degree and timing of the decrepitude, but death itself is always a matter of chance; it may be a sudden accident or heart failure. The only thing that happens with increasing senescence is that the chances of death increase. In fact life insurance tables are constructed upon life expectancy, which in effect is the probability of dying during any one period in one's life, and the older the years, the greater the likelihood because of the gene-controlled senescence. The one exception to this trend in humans is right after birth when the trauma of entering the world leaves the infant in a dangerous and susceptible condition; but this early period of low life expectancy quickly disappears as childhood begins.

There is another aspect to aging that is ecological or environmental and leads us over to the next subject. With the increased medical care of this century, the life expectancy has become greatly extended. In Elizabethan England there were virtually no old people, but now they represent a large part of the world population, at least, in countries with efficient medical services. This change in the average age of any population has had many effects, especially economic ones connected with retirement and care that are still troubling us. The presence of old people probably even affects the selective forces acting upon any human population even though the aged themselves do not reproduce. In essence, we have on a statistical basis altered the gene-controlled life expectancy, and one must expect both social and evolutionary changes, although they may be of such a complex nature that their analysis will be difficult.

ECOLOGY

The most significant feature of man's ecology, as we have already illustrated in the previous example, is that to a large extent he can alter it to suit (or sometimes damage) his own purposes. He wants to live longer, so he improves his medical care. He is cold, so he builds a house, lights a furnace, and puts on his long winter underwear. In this way he has been able to do all the things animals have taken millions of years of selection and evolution to do. He can live in the tropics, in the arctic, in the desert, or in the rain forest or anywhere in between these extremes. He can fly; he can travel on or under water; he can move rivers to make power; he can mold the environment about him to suit his whims, his greed, his common sense, and his humanity. All these remarkable aspects come from extended embryonic development and increase in brain size.

Some animals can also modify their environment. The beaver needs high water for protection, house building, and winter feeding, so he builds a dam. Bird nests are insulated and serve as a useful isolation device against the raw environment. The difference, as before, is a matter of degree; man is so much better at it. He is so because he has the ability of invention and imagination, and once the new idea has spawned it can be carried down directly to the next generation. The beaver's dam-building behavior is to a far greater extent genetically determined and, therefore, rigid and slow to progress. This would be even more the case with insect nests, such as some of the large termite nests that are beautifully constructed to control the temperature and humidity for the colony inside.

This progressive improvement of methods of environment-modifying will have another effect upon human evolution. It means that there is no longer the possibility of climatic factors producing strong selective forces. To put it crudely, the climate inside an air-conditioned house is the same all over the world. So, what with the great intermixture and crossbreeding that is going on in the world at the moment and the beginning of a disappearance of climatic factors as selective influences, we can expect that the production of new species of man is becoming less and less likely, and, therefore, the genetic evolution of man will progress exceedingly slowly.

Another striking way man keeps altering his environment is by altering his relation with other animals and plants. In the first place he is waging a constant war against his parasites. As civilization advances, the number of communities that live in quiet resignation and balance with their bacterial, protozoan, and worm parasites steadily decreases. The variety of specific medical tricks to combat these enemies becomes more formidable every day. The danger lies only in that, with fewer parasites, we have fewer immunities and that with mutation among microorganisms we must be ever vigilant for a sudden epidemic spread of new virulence. The fact that the parasites are being removed does undoubtedly change the selection forces upon human beings. As an example, if malaria is totally eliminated from Africa—not an unreasonable possibility for the future—then the selection pressure to maintain the sickle-cell anemia genes will disappear, and in turn the gene itself will presumably be selected out of the population. This may occur at a very slow rate, but the fact that the homozygotes do not live can no longer be outweighed by any advantage to be derived from the heterozygous condition.

Besides modifying his parasites man has also done extraordinary things in the modification of animals and plants to provide more abundant food. The domestication of animals and then the selective breeding of animals and plants to produce a higher yield have been steadily rewarding processes for centuries. Even recently the discovery by G. H. Shull and E. M. East—that if two purebred (homozygous) strains of corn were crossbred, the first generation would show a marked hybrid vigor—has meant an incredible gain in the yield of corn. The amount of milk per cow, eggs per chickens, meat per pig, etc., seem to rise steadily as the science of agriculture advances.

But man's relation to wild animals and plants is not so happy. The urge to shoot, saw down, and plunder his natural environment until it is almost beyond repair seems to be a persistent characteristic of man. It is the frontier spirit, which is all very well when one man is free to take his food from millions of acres of wilderness; but the tide is turning, at first slowly, then rapidly, and soon there will be many men on one acre, and all the birds, the plants, and the mammals are bound to suffer. Admittedly to some extent our worries about the loss are sentimental, but then there is no sin to such a sentiment; it deserves respect even though it may have no meaning in dollars.

Conservation has practical meaning, too. Certain commodities on the surface of the earth are limited in their supply. Minerals, oil, coal, in fact everything that is brought up out of the soil is finite in quantity. Even the crops that can be replenished, such as woodland or arable soil, can be lost if care is not taken to restore what is taken. Mostly the proper care is not exerted, although our consciousness of it and all these problems is steadily increasing. The worry is that besides material the world will run out of available energy and we all will be bankrupt. It is hoped that, should this happen, salvation will come from the harnessing of atomic energy, which exists in virtually unlimited supply; but the grave question of which we are all so fearful and uncertain is: can mankind show sufficient maturity to use atomic energy in this way, or will the old frontier spirit insist on more excitement and more sudden release of atomic energy? The collective thoughts of governments and peoples are hard to manage; this is one bit of human ecology that is little understood.

All these difficulties that beset man at the moment have one key factor. It is that the number of people on the earth is growing at an extraordinary pace. It is not just that overpopulation will effect the selection rate of different genes; the success or disaster of our future will be decided much sooner than that. Overpopulation has created problems that, not only biologically. have never been encountered in man or his ancestors; they have never even been encountered culturally or historically in the proportions they are now assuming. We have absolutely no concept of how to cope with them.

Some of the overpopulation has occurred in nonindustrialized countries, such as China or India, although China is forcing itself through ruthless deprivation to become industrialized. Other countries, the Western countries in general, became overpopulated as part of the industrialization process. The end result in both cases is a vast economic maze in which the supply of food and goods and their stable purchase and consumption is complex beyond imagination. The world today is utterly dependent upon the gigantic commercial system that has arisen because of the size of the world population. It has come into being so rapidly that we understand it poorly, and as the population further increases it will change again and again.

We seem to be caught in a mesh of forward progression, and we do not even know if we are going in the right direction or the wrong; and were we convinced it is wrong there seems little to be done about it. We can only hope that just as nature is balanced the forces that affect us will keep some sort of equilibrium and that it is maintained gently and calmly and not by violent changes. Change and progress we expect, and we expect them to be rapid since historical rather than selective evolution is largely concerned; let it not become too rapid, for we sorely yearn for orderly change and not catastrophe.

FURTHER READING

The books and papers listed in this bibliography are no more than a few suggestions for further reading. In every case an attempt has been made to indicate if the work is popular or difficult, interesting or merely comprehensive, or has any other helpful characteristic.

The page numbers on the left of each reference refer to pages in the text so that it is possible to go from here to the text and back again with the minimum of confusion, and at the same time prevent the text from being bespeckled with footnotes.

CHAPTER 1: THE CELL

PAGE 1—It would be a sacrilege in citing references to the subject of cytology not to begin with one of the great books of biology, E. B. Wilson, *The Cell in Development and Heredity* (Macmillan, 1928). However, it must be quickly emphasized that while some of this large book is pertinent to this chapter, much of it applies to the later chapters on development and genetics. Also the advances in the last forty years have been very significant, and, therefore, Wilson's book is really a summary of the first grand period of cytology. Since we are right now so much in the middle of a period of active development, it is hard to find a modern equivalent of Wilson's book, although L. E. R. Picken, *The Organization of Cells and other Organisms* (Oxford, 1960), is a most comprehensive volume and filled with a great variety of useful information. Also J. Brachet, *Biochemical Cytology* (Academic Press, 1957), is a very lucid account, as the name implies, of the modern biochemical aspects. But none of these books are popular reading; they all are technical treatises. There are no comprehensive treatises of modern cytology for the layman, although a number of excellent articles have appeared on specific points, some of which will be mentioned. The possible exception to this might be R. W. Gerard, *Unresting Cells* (Harper, 1940), which is a simple presentation of problems of cells and their activities.

PAGE 6—If there is interest in further information about Brownian motion, kinetic theory of gases, and energy, any textbook of physics and physical chemistry will be helpful—for instance, E. M. Rogers, *Physics for the Enquiring Mind* (Princeton, 1960).

PAGE 8—Major new developments on the subject of photosynthesis are constantly appearing. See D. J. Arnon, *Scientific American, 203,* 104–118 (November, 1960) for a review of some important recent discoveries. The earlier work is well summarized by E. I. Rábinowitch, *Scientific American, 189,* 80–84 (November, 1953) and *179,* 24–35 (August, 1948).

PAGE 9—The whole subject of biochemistry is concerned primarily with the matters discussed here. There are many good books on biochemistry although this is not a subject for casual dabbling. A good solid text is J. S. Fruton and S. Simonds, *General Biochemistry* (Wiley, 1958). See also A. C. Giese, *Cell Physiology* (Saunders, 1957).

PAGE 11—The subject of cell movement is one of continuous interest. For a recent survey of the problem of amoeboid movement see a review by R. D. Allen in J. Brachet and A. E. Mirsky, eds. *The Cell,* Vol. II, (Academic Press, 1961). The most significant advances in muscle contraction have been made by A. Szent-Györgyi, *The Chemistry of Muscular Contraction,* 2nd ed. (Academic Press, 1951). See also H. E. Huxley, *Scientific American, 199,* 66–82 (November, 1958) for some stimulating ideas on how the chemistry might fit in with the structure of muscle.

PAGE 11—Sensory or nerve physiology is adequately discussed in many textbooks. See, for instance, L. V. Heilbrunn, *An Outline of General Physiology,* 3rd ed. (Saunders, 1952).

PAGE 13—Some of the striking results of electron microscopy in revealing cell structure are shown in *Electron Microscopy,* edited by F. S. Sjöstrand and J. Rhodin (Academic Press, 1957). See also the *Fourth International Conference in Electron Microscopy,* Vol. II, Biology and Medicine, edited by W. Bargmann, D. Peters, and C. Wolpers (Springer, 1960). Both these books are a series of highly technical papers, but they are accompanied by first-rate electron micrographs.

PAGE 15—The structure and the chemical activities of mitochondria are discussed by P. Siekevitz, *Scientific American, 197,* 131–140 (July, 1957).

CHAPTER 2: EVOLUTION

PAGE 19—The study of viruses (or virology) is a very active field of interest that changes rapidly. As a beginning a short statement by N. D. Zinder, *American Scientist, 48,* 608–612 (1960), brings the subject up to date and refers to a number of recent books on the subject.

PAGE 19—The structure and activities of bacteria are described in many textbooks of bacteriology (or microbiology), which usually include a discussion of viruses. A good example (which also has a section on sexuality and recombination in bacteria) is R. V. Stanier, M. Doudoroff, and E. A. Adelberg, *The Microbial World* (Prentice-Hall, 1957).

PAGE 24—One of the pioneers in the problem of the origin of life is A. I. Oparin, whose book *The Origin of Life on Earth,* 3rd ed. (Oliver & Boyd, 1957), is of lasting importance. In recent years there has been increasing interest in the problem. See, for instance, the symposium edited by M. Florkin, *Aspects of the Origin of Life* (Pergamon Press, 1960).

PAGE 25—The whole subject of invertebrate zoology is dealt with in a masterfully simple way in R. M. Buchsbaum, *Animals without Backbones,* rev. ed. (Chicago, 1957), and both the beginner and even the more advanced student will find the book very useful. For a far more complete discussion the reader is referred to the classic series by L. H. Hyman, *The Invertebrates.* The first volume, *Protozoa through Ctenophora* (McGraw-Hill, 1940), will be particularly applicable to much that is discussed here.

PAGE 27—See G. M. Smith, *Cryptogamic Botany,* 2 vols., 2nd ed. (McGraw-Hill, 1955), for an authoritative and up-to-date discussion of slime molds and other lower plants.

PAGE 33—The subjects of plant anatomy and physiology, as well as the evolution of the higher plants, is the material of many excellent general botany textbooks. See, for instance, H. J. Fuller and O. Tippo, *College Botany,* rev. ed. (Holt, 1955).

PAGE 36—Again see G. M. Smith, *Cryptogamic Botany*, Vol. I, 2nd ed., McGraw-Hill (1955), for a discussion of the fungi. Another book that can be highly recommended as good and interesting reading is J. Ramsbottom, *Mushrooms and Toadstools* (Collins, 1954).

PAGE 37—The subject of the origin and evolution of multicellular animals is one of long and continued interest to zoologists. See L. H. Hyman, *The Invertebrates* (McGraw-Hill, 1940) *et seq*. The same applies for the evolution of different groups of multicellular plants. See G. M. Smith, *Cryptogamic Botany* 2 vols., 2nd ed. (McGraw-Hill, 1955). In the past the difficulties and uncertainties of such speculations have been inadequately emphasized, although that has now been corrected in a sobering little book by G. A. Kerkut, *Implications of Evolution* (Pergamon, 1960). Various important evolutionary schemes for animals are discussed critically, and the end result is a clear indication that the details of the family tree of man's invertebrate ancestors are somewhat in doubt, to say the least. (This, incidentally, is the reason for the absence of arrows in Figure 7.)

PAGE 39—Vertebrate evolution, largely because of the excellent fossil record, is better understood than that of invertebrates. The sequence is described in vivid terms by the noted paleontologist, A. S. Romer, in his *Man and the Vertebrates* (Penguin, 1954).

PAGE 44—Some of the best writing in biology has gone into the subject of Darwinism, and there are many good books to recommend. The paleontologist's approach is seen in a fine book by G. G. Simpson, *The Meaning of Evolution,* (Yale, 1949), in which the first section of the book is applicable. Another thoughtful and somewhat more difficult review is that of J. M. Smith, *The Theory of Evolution* (Penguin, 1958). See also W. H. Dowdeswell, *The Mechanism of Evolution,* (Harper, 1960). In these books there are many references to further writing on the subject, and prominent names to look for are: T. Dobzhansky, R. A. Fisher, E. B. Ford, J. B. S. Haldane, J. S. Huxley, E. Mayr, B. Rensch, G. G. Simpson, G. L. Stebbins, C. H. Waddington.

PAGE 44—For a history of genetics, cytology, and evolution, see E. Nordenskiöld, *The History of Biology* (Tudor, 1942).

PAGE 46—The work of H. B. D. Kettlewell on the rise of dark forms of moths in industrial areas is described by himself in *Scientific American, 200,* 48–53 (March, 1959). Also a vivid description of the experiments, along with many other matters of interest on the subject of animal behavior, will be found in N. Tinbergen's scientific autobiography, *Curious Naturalists* (Basic Books, 1960).

PAGE 49—The finches of the Galápagos have been reinvestigated in an important study by D. Lack, *Darwin's Finches* (Harper Torchbooks, 1961).

PAGE 49—An authoritative technical discussion of species formation will be found in E. Mayr, *Systematics and the Origin of Species* (Columbia, 1942).

PAGE 52—An equally technical and authoritative discussion of the evolution of the major groups is to be found in B. Rensch, *Evolution above the Species Level* (Columbia, 1960).

CHAPTER 3: GENETICS

PAGE 54—A number of the topics examined in the first few pages of this chapter are discussed in detail in W. Braun, *Bacterial Genetics* (Saunders, 1953). This includes a careful examination of mutation and selection in bacteria along with the mutagenic effect of radiation and chemical agents.

PAGE 55—The discovery and detailed examination of the process of transformation in bacteria is also described by Braun.

PAGE 56—The subject of substitutes for sex, that is, variation shuffling mechanisms other than sex, are discussed in a short, compact essay by J. B. S. Haldane in *New Biology*, no. 19, 7–26 (1955). For a more detailed discussion of this kind of shuffling in slime molds see J. T. Bonner, *The Evolution of Development* (Cambridge, 1958).

PAGE 57—Most any textbook of biology will have an adequate description of the elements of meiosis and mitosis. For a more detailed description see E. B. Wilson, *The Cell in Development and Heredity* (Macmillan, 1928), or the more recent and advanced book of C. P. Swanson, *Cytology and Cytogenetics* (Prentice-Hall, 1957).

PAGE 58—There are many excellent discussions of Mendel's laws that are the basic elements of genetics. There are numerous textbooks, or the reader might find T. Dobzhansky, *Evolution, Genetics and Man* (Wiley, 1955), a clear and readable presentation.

PAGE 63—These comments also apply for the discoveries of Morgan and his co-workers (of which Dobzhansky was one). This book also has good suggestions for further reading.

PAGE 64—While Dobzhansky's book also briefly discusses polyploidy as a means of variation in plants, a detailed and authoritative discussion of this subject will be found in G. L. Stebbins *Variation and Evolution in Plants* (Columbia, 1950).

PAGE 64—One of the significant contributions in modern evolutionary genetics is C. D. Darlington, *Evolution of Genetic Systems,* 2nd ed. (Oliver and Boyd, 1958). It is a difficult and sophisticated book in which as its title indicates, he shows that the shuffling system itself has undergone evolutionary progress.

PAGE 66—Concerning the chemical nature of the gene, there have been a number of recent books. See, for instance, C. B. Anfinsen, *The Molecular Basis of Evolution* (Wiley, 1959), which discusses among other things the work of S. Benzer. See also S. Zamenhof, *The Chemistry of Heredity* (C. C. Thomas, 1959).

PAGE 67—The effects of genes are discussed in various texts. See, for instance, C. H. Waddington, *An Introduction to Modern Genetics* (Macmillan, 1939), and A. M. Srb and R. D. Owen, *General Genetics* (Freeman, 1952).

PAGE 68—T. Dobzhansky, *Evolution, Genetics and Man* (Wiley, 1955), gives a good introduction to evolutionary genetics. For a more advanced discussion see his *Genetics and the Origin of Species,* 3rd ed. (Columbia, 1951). Also many of the topics discussed in this and the following pages are considered for plants in G. L. Stebbins, *Variation and Evolution in Plants* (Columbia, 1950). This book is especially helpful on matters of variation and environment, the evolutionary significance of the loss of sexual reproduction, inbreeding and crossbreeding, and incompatibility mechanisms. For this latter subject see also the essays of C. D. Darlington and K. Mather, *Genes, Plants and People* (Allen & Unwin, 1950).

PAGE 69—For a general discussion of the mathematical approach to evolutionary genetics see T. Dobzhansky, *Genetics and the Origin of Species,* 3rd ed. (Columbia, 1951). See also D. Falconer, *Introduction to Quantitative Genetics* (Oliver & Boyd, 1960).

PAGE 74—R. Goldschmidt is one of the strong proponents of macromutations, as he describes in his *The Material Basis of Evolution* (Yale, 1940). The opposing view and a general discussion of the subject is well presented in B. Rensch's *Evolution above the Species Level* (Columbia, 1960).

CHAPTER 4: DEVELOPMENT

PAGE 77—The points raised here concerning the relation of development, genetics, and evolution have been examined in much greater detail in J. T. Bonner, *Evolution of Development* (Cambridge, 1958).

PAGE 79—Any modern text in genetics will have a good discussion of biochemical genetics. See, for instance, A. M. Srb and R. D. Owen, *General Genetics* (Freeman, 1952). If an advanced and sophisticated account is desired, R. P. Wagner and H. K. Mitchell, *Genetics and Metabolism* (Wiley, 1955), is recommended, or for recent reviews see, W. D. McElroy and B. Glass, eds., *The Chemical Basis of Heredity* (Hopkins, 1958).

PAGE 82—The linear order of the genes on a bacterial chromosome was discovered by P. E. Hartman and M. Demerec and is described briefly by C. B. Anfinsen in *The Molecular Basis of Evolution* (Wiley, 1959).

PAGE 83—J. S. Hämmerling discusses much of his own work in the *International Review of Cytology, 2,* 475–498 (1953).

PAGE 84—For an excellent, detailed review of this subject see R. Briggs and T. J. King in J. Brachet and A. F. Mirsky, eds., *The Cell,* Vol. 1 (Academic Press, 1959), chapter 13.

PAGE 86—The discovery of these chromosome puffs is credited to W. Beerman and C. Pavan. For a technical review see chapter five in D. Rudnick, ed., *Developmental Cytology* (Ronald, 1959).

PAGE 86—The analysis of the processes of development that begins here and goes on for a number of pages follows in outline the more detailed account of J. T. Bonner, *Morphogenesis* (Princeton Press, 1952). The reader may find in that volume further references to the processes of growth, morphogenetic movement, and differentiation.

PAGE 94—For a most interesting and readable account of relative growth see the pioneering account of J. S. Huxley, *Problems of Relative Growth* (Methuen, 1932).

PAGE 94—There is a good brief discussion of R. Goldschmidt's work in Chapter 3 of G. R. de Beer, *Embryos and Ancestors,* 3rd ed. (Oxford, 1958). Goldschmidt himself has written extensively on the subject, and see his *Physiological Genetics,* (McGraw-Hill, 1938), and his *Theoretical Genetics* (California, 1955).

PAGE 100—The recent work on cell re-aggregation has been reviewed in a popular essay by one of the pioneers in the field, A. Moscona, *Scientific American, 200,* 132–144 (May, 1959). Another good general discussion, with further references, will be found in N. J. Berrill, *Growth, Development and Pattern* (Freeman, 1961).

PAGE 104—H. Spemann's own book describing his studies and all the early work on induction remains a classic: *Embryonic Development and Induction* (Yale, 1938). For more recent work see J. Holtfreter, *Growth, 15* (suppl.), 117–152 (1951), and C. Grobstein, in D. Rudnick, ed., *Aspects of Synthesis and Order in Growth* (Princeton, 1954), chapter 10.

PAGE 106—The whole subject of the timing of gene effects is admirably treated in G. R. de Beer, *Embryos and Ancestors,* 3rd ed. (Oxford, 1958).

CHAPTER 5: SIMPLE TO COMPLEX

PAGE 110—Beginning here and in the pages that follow there is a general discussion of the structure and the functioning of higher plants, with special emphasis on energy conversion, reproduction, and coordination. This subject is one treated in any elementary botany textbook. See for instance, H. J. Fuller and O. Tippo, *College Botany,* rev. ed. (Holt, 1955), or A. Cronquist, *Introductory Botany* (Harper, 1961). At the more advanced level, on the functional or physiological side, *Principles of Plant Physiology* (Freeman, 1952), by James Bonner and A. W. Galston is recommended.

PAGE 111—Again the subject of predaceous plants is part of any botany text. A detailed account may be found in F. E. Lloyd, *Carnivorous Plants* (Chronica Botanica, 1942).

PAGE 113—Mammalian digestion, gas exchange, and circulation are discussed briefly in elementary zoology and biology texts. They are, however, intensively examined in animal physiology textbooks. A good example is A. J. Carlson and V. Johnson, *Machinery of the Body* (Chicago, 1937).

PAGE 116—The subject of fertilization is one of continuing interest to the research biologist. For a recent survey of some of the work written for the layman see an article by R. D. Allen, *Scientific American, 201,* 124–134 (July, 1959). For a more comprehensive and detailed account see Lord Rothschild, *Fertilization* (Methuen, 1956).

PAGE 117—Nervous conduction is also an integral part of the animal physiology books mentioned above.

PAGE 118—The subject of size and its effect on living organisms is a very ancient one beginning with Archimedes and Galileo. The subject is dealt with in a masterful fashion by D'Arcy W. Thompson, *On Growth and Form,* abridged ed., (Cambridge, 1961), chapter two. For a general discussion of the relation of size to division of labor see J. T. Bonner, *Morphogenesis* (Princeton, 1952), chapter two.

Page 119—The arguments of B. Rensch on the evolutionary advantages of increased brain size and discussed in his *Evolution above the Species Level* (Columbia, 1960). He has also written a popular essay on this subject in the *Scientific American, 196,* 44–49 (February, 1957).

Page 122—The progressive elaboration of the hydroids is discussed in a simplified manner in R. Buchsbaum, *Animals without Backbones* (Chicago, 1948), and in a more detailed fashion in L. H. Hyman's *The Invertebrates,* vol. 1 (McGraw-Hill, 1940).

Page 125—Animal communication is a subject of intense interest in recent years. Good sources of information are two books by N. Tinbergen, *Social Behavior in Animals* (Methuen, 1953), and *The Study of Instinct* (Oxford, 1951).

Page 126—N. Tinbergen describes his experiments on gulls in detail in a delightful and readable book, *The Herring Gull's World* (Basic Books, 1961).

Page 130—One of the most fluent and literate biologists of all time is W. M. Wheeler, and one of his best books is *Social Life Among the Insects* (Harcourt, Brace, 1923). In it he describes a wide variety of insect societies.

Page 130—An interesting summary for the layman of some of M. Lüscher's work is given in his article in the *Scientific American, 188,* 74–76 (1953).

Page 132—A good summary of the work on army ants is given by T. C. Schneirla and G. Piel, *Scientific American, 187,* 16–23 (1948). Some of the actual work and a complete set of references may be found in T. C. Schneirla and R. F. Brown, *Bulletin of the American Museum of Natural History, 95,* 267–353 (1950).

Page 132—The great work of K. von Frisch is described in *The Dancing Bees* (Harcourt, Brace, 1955).

Page 133—For a general discussion of social mammals see J. T. Bonner, *Cells and Societies* (Princeton, 1955), in which further references are given for works on fur seals and deer.

Page 134—For the study of Scottish red deer the reader is urged to go to a most interesting book by F. F. Darling, *A Herd of Red Deer* (Oxford, 1937).

PAGE 135—And an equally interesting account of the habits of wolves is given by A. Murie, *The Wolves of Mount McKinley,* Fauna of National Parks of U. S. Fauna Series, no. 5 (1944).

PAGE 135—On baboons the reader will find profit in S. Zuckerman's, *The Social Life of Monkeys and Apes* (Harcourt, Brace, 1932).

PAGE 136—For a good discussion of *Parasitism and Symbiosis* (Sidgwick and Jackson, 1952)—this translation of a book of the well-known French biologist M. Caullery is recommended.

PAGE 139—Guests in ant colonies are discussed in W. M. Wheeler's book mentioned above.

PAGE 140—For a good discussion of communities and some further references see G. G. Simpson, C. S. Pittendrigh, and C. F. Tiffany, *Life* (Harcourt, Brace, 1957), part seven.

PAGE 140—Invasions of foreign species are discussed in detail in C. S. Elton, *The Ecology of Invasions by Animals and Plants* (Methuen, 1958).

CHAPTER 6: MAN

PAGE 142—See W. W. Howells, *Mankind in the Making* (Doubleday, 1959), for an excellent and readable discussion of man and his ancestors.

PAGE 143—And for a discussion of early, prehistoric cultural evolution, see an equally fine book by the same author: W. W. Howells, *Back of History* (Doubleday, 1954).

PAGE 143—W. H. Thorpe, in his *Learning and Instinct in Animals* (Methuen, 1956), gives a technical review of experiments on instinct and learning. It is a rich source of references of original papers. The book of N. Tinbergen, *The Study of Instinct* (Oxford, 1951), is again a technical book, but an absorbing one that gives a comprehensive view of the new school of animal behavior, sometimes called ethology. As mentioned in the last chapter, for a discussion of the work of T. C. Schneirla see his popular essay with G. Piel in *Scientific American, 187,* 16–23 (1948).

PAGE 144—H. and M. Frings have described their work on crow dialects in an interesting article in *Scientific American, 201,* 119–131 (November, 1959).

PAGE 146—The evidence for the inheritance of behavioral patterns, such as intelligence and various emotional qualities for both man and animals (including dogs) is reviewed in the detailed study of J. L. Fuller and W. R. Thomson, *Behavior Genetics* (Wiley, 1960).

PAGE 148—For a most absorbing yet technical and detailed discussion of bowerbirds see A. J. Marshall, *Bower Birds* (Oxford, 1954). Marshall has also written a short essay (with excellent illustrations) in *Scientific American, 195,* 48–52 (June, 1956).

PAGE 151—There are many books that touch on the subject of genetics in man, but the first one to consider is Curt Stern, *Principles of Human Genetics,* 2nd ed. (Freeman, 1960). This is an authoritative text by one of the foremost and most thoughtful geneticists. A more general book by another distinguished geneticist that covers a number of subjects discussed in this book is T. Dobzhansky, *Evolution, Genetics, and Man* (Wiley, 1955). The matter of the adaptiveness of white and dark skin is examined critically by H. F. Blum, *Quarterly Review of Biology, 36,* 50–63 (1961).

PAGE 154—Skin transplantation and twins are discussed in an eloquent essay by P. B. Medawar, *The Uniqueness of the Individual* (Methuen, 1957), in which he describes the work that led ultimately to his receiving the Nobel prize.

PAGE 155—This study of police dogs recognizing twins was done by H. Kalmus, *British Journal of Animal Behavior, 3,* 25–31 (1955).

PAGE 156—G. R. de Beer, *Embryos and Ancestors,* 3rd ed. (Oxford 1958), gives a difficult but rewarding discussion of the timing of different parts of development and the consequences of shifts in this timing. The consequences as far as man is concerned are discussed in a popular essay by J. Rostand, *Life, the Great Adventure* (Scribners, 1956).

PAGE 157—Senescence is elegantly discussed in two essays in P. B. Medawar, *The Uniqueness of the Individual* (Methuen, 1957). For a more detailed analysis and a list of references see A. Comfort, *The Biology of Senescence* (Rinehart, 1956).

PAGE 158—A new book by the well-known biologist and writer M. Bates, *Man in Nature* (Prentice-Hall, 1961), considers many of the matters discussed in this chapter including a consideration of human ecology from a biologist's point of view.

PAGE 160—There are many books on conservation, but L. J. and M. Milne, *The Balance of Nature* (Knopf, 1960), is interesting and has many references for further reading.

PAGE 161—The problem of world population is discussed many places. M. Bates, *Prevalence of People* (Scribners, 1955), does an excellent job of looking at the problem with the perspective of a biologist.

GLOSSARY–INDEX

Revised February 1966

harper torchbooks

HUMANITIES AND SOCIAL SCIENCES

American Studies: General

THOMAS C. COCHRAN: The Inner Revolution: *Essays on the Social Sciences in History* TB/1140

EDWARD S. CORWIN: American Constitutional History. *Essays edited by Alpheus T. Mason and Gerald Garvey* TB/1136

CARL N. DEGLER, Ed.: Pivotal Interpretations of American History TB/1240, TB/1241

A. HUNTER DUPREE: Science in the Federal Government: *A History of Policies and Activities to 1940* TB/573

OSCAR HANDLIN, Ed.: This Was America: *As Recorded by European Travelers in the Eighteenth, Nineteenth and Twentieth Centuries. Illus.* TB/1119

MARCUS LEE HANSEN: The Atlantic Migration: 1607-1860. *Edited by Arthur M. Schlesinger. Introduction by Oscar Handlin* TB/1052

MARCUS LEE HANSEN: The Immigrant in American History. *Edited with a Foreword by Arthur M. Schlesinger* TB/1120

JOHN HIGHAM, Ed.: The Reconstruction of American History TB/1068

ROBERT H. JACKSON: The Supreme Court in the American System of Government TB/1106

JOHN F. KENNEDY: A Nation of Immigrants. *Illus. Revised and Enlarged. Introduction by Robert F. Kennedy* TB/1118

RALPH BARTON PERRY: Puritanism and Democracy TB/1138

ARNOLD ROSE: The Negro in America: *The Condensed Version of Gunnar Myrdal's* An American Dilemma TB/3048

MAURICE R. STEIN: The Eclipse of Community: *An Interpretation of American Studies* TB/1128

W. LLOYD WARNER and Associates: Democracy in Jonesville: *A Study in Quality and Inequality* || TB/1129

W. LLOYD WARNER: Social Class in America: *The Evaluation of Status* TB/1013

American Studies: Colonial

BERNARD BAILYN, Ed.: The Apologia of Robert Keayne: *Self-Portrait of a Puritan Merchant* TB/1201

BERNARD BAILYN: The New England Merchants in the Seventeenth Century TB/1149

JOSEPH CHARLES: The Origins of the American Party System TB/1049

LAWRENCE HENRY GIPSON: The Coming of the Revolution: 1763-1775. † *Illus.* TB/3007

LEONARD W. LEVY: Freedom of Speech and Press in Early American History: *Legacy of Suppression* TB/1109

PERRY MILLER: Errand Into the Wilderness TB/1139

PERRY MILLER & T. H. JOHNSON, Eds.: The Puritans: *A Sourcebook of Their Writings* Vol. I TB/1093; Vol. II TB/1094

EDMUND S. MORGAN, Ed.: The Diary of Michael Wigglesworth, 1653-1657: *The Conscience of a Puritan*

EDMUND S. MORGAN: The Puritan Family: *Religion and Domestic Relations in Seventeenth-Century New England* TB/1227

RICHARD B. MORRIS: Government and Labor in Early America TB/1244

KENNETH B. MURDOCK: Literature and Theology in Colonial New England TB/99

WALLACE NOTESTEIN: The English People on the Eve of Colonization: 1603-1630. † *Illus.* TB/3006

LOUIS B. WRIGHT: The Cultural Life of the American Colonies: 1607-1763. † *Illus.* TB/3005

American Studies: From the Revolution to 1860

JOHN R. ALDEN: The American Revolution: 1775-1783. † *Illus.* TB/3011

MAX BELOFF, Ed.: The Debate on the American Revolution, 1761-1783: *A Sourcebook* TB/1225

RAY A. BILLINGTON: The Far Western Frontier: 1830-1860. † *Illus.* TB/3012

EDMUND BURKE: On the American Revolution: *Selected Speeches and Letters. ‡ Edited by Elliott Robert Barkan* TB/3068

WHITNEY R. CROSS: The Burned-Over District: *The Social and Intellectual History of Enthusiastic Religion in Western New York, 1800-1850* TB/1242

GEORGE DANGERFIELD: The Awakening of American Nationalism: 1815-1828. † *Illus.* TB/3061

CLEMENT EATON: The Freedom-of-Thought Struggle in the Old South. *Revised and Enlarged. Illus.* TB/1150

CLEMENT EATON: The Growth of Southern Civilization: 1790-1860. † *Illus.* TB/3040

LOUIS FILLER: The Crusade Against Slavery: 1830-1860. † *Illus.* TB/3029

DIXON RYAN FOX: The Decline of Aristocracy in the Politics of New York: 1801-1840. ‡ *Edited by Robert V. Remini* TB/3064

FELIX GILBERT: The Beginnings of American Foreign Policy: *To the Farewell Address* TB/1200

FRANCIS J. GRUND: Aristocracy in America: *Social Class in the Formative Years of the New Nation* TB/1001

ALEXANDER HAMILTON: The Reports of Alexander Hamilton. ‡ *Edited by Jacob E. Cooke* TB/3060

THOMAS JEFFERSON: Notes on the State of Virginia. ‡ *Edited by Thomas P. Abernethy* TB/3052

JAMES MADISON: The Forging of American Federalism: *Selected Writings of James Madison. Edited by Saul K. Padover* TB/1226

† The New American Nation Series, edited by Henry Steele Commager and Richard B. Morris.

‡ American Perspectives series, edited by Bernard Wishy and William E. Leuchtenburg.

* The Rise of Modern Europe series, edited by William L. Langer.

|| Researches in the Social, Cultural, and Behavioral Sciences, edited by Benjamin Nelson.

§ The Library of Religion and Culture, edited by Benjamin Nelson.

Σ Harper Modern Science Series, edited by James R. Newman.

° Not for sale in Canada.

BERNARD MAYO: Myths and Men: *Patrick Henry, George Washington, Thomas Jefferson* TB/1108

JOHN C. MILLER: Alexander Hamilton and the Growth of the New Nation TB/3057

RICHARD B. MORRIS, Ed.: The Era of the American Revolution TB/1180

R. B. NYE: The Cultural Life of the New Nation: 1776-1801. † *Illus.* TB/3026

FRANCIS S. PHILBRICK: The Rise of the West, 1754-1830. † *Illus.* TB/3067

TIMOTHY L. SMITH: Revivalism and Social Reform: *Protestantism on the Eve of the Civil War* TB/1229

FRANK THISTLETHWAITE: America and the Atlantic Community: *Anglo-American Aspects, 1790-1850* TB/1107

A. F. TYLER: Freedom's Ferment: *Phases of American Social History from the Revolution to the Outbreak of the Civil War. 31 illus.* TB/1074

GLYNDON G. VAN DEUSEN: The Jacksonian Era: 1828-1848. † *Illus.* TB/3028

LOUIS B. WRIGHT: Culture on the Moving Frontier TB/1053

American Studies: The Civil War to 1900

THOMAS C. COCHRAN & WILLIAM MILLER: The Age of Enterprise: *A Social History of Industrial America* TB/1054

W. A. DUNNING: Essays on the Civil War and Reconstruction. *Introduction by David Donald* TB/1181

W. A. DUNNING: Reconstruction, Political and Economic: 1865-1877 TB/1073

HAROLD U. FAULKNER: Politics, Reform and Expansion: 1890-1900. † *Illus.* TB/3020

HELEN HUNT JACKSON: A Century of Dishonor: *The Early Crusade for Indian Reform. ‡ Edited by Andrew F. Rolle* TB/3063

ALBERT D. KIRWAN: Revolt of the Rednecks: *Mississippi Politics, 1876-1925* TB/1199

ROBERT GREEN MCCLOSKEY: American Conservatism in the Age of Enterprise: 1865-1910 TB/1137

WHITELAW REID: After the War: *A Tour of the Southern States, 1865-1866. ‡ Edited by C. Vann Woodward* TB/3066

CHARLES H. SHINN: Mining Camps: *A Study in American Frontier Government. ‡ Edited by Rodman W. Paul* TB/3062

VERNON LANE WHARTON: The Negro in Mississippi: 1865-1890 TB/1178

American Studies: 1900 to the Present

RAY STANNARD BAKER: Following the Color Line: *American Negro Citizenship in Progressive Era. ‡ Illus. Edited by Dewey W. Grantham, Jr.* TB/3053

RANDOLPH S. BOURNE: War and the Intellectuals: *Collected Essays, 1915-1919. ‡ Ed. by Carl Resek* TB/3043

A. RUSSELL BUCHANAN: The United States and World War II. † *Illus.* Vol. I TB/3044; Vol. II TB/3045

ABRAHAM CAHAN: The Rise of David Levinsky: *a documentary novel of social mobility in early twentieth century America. Intro. by John Higham* TB/1028

THOMAS C. COCHRAN: The American Business System: *A Historical Perspective, 1900-1955* TB/1080

FOSTER RHEA DULLES: America's Rise to World Power: 1898-1954. † *Illus.* TB/3021

JOHN D. HICKS: Republican Ascendancy: 1921-1933. † *Illus.* TB/3041

SIDNEY HOOK: Reason, Social Myths, and Democracy TB/1237

ROBERT HUNTER: Poverty: *Social Conscience in the Progressive Era. ‡ Edited by Peter d'A. Jones* TB/3065

WILLIAM L. LANGER & S. EVERETT GLEASON: The Challenge to Isolation: *The World Crisis of 1937-1940 and American Foreign Policy* Vol. I TB/3054; Vol. II TB/3055

WILLIAM E. LEUCHTENBURG: Franklin D. Roosevelt and the New Deal: 1932-1940. † *Illus.* TB/3025

ARTHUR S. LINK: Woodrow Wilson and the Progressive Era: 1910-1917. † *Illus.* TB/3023

GEORGE E. MOWRY: The Era of Theodore Roosevelt and the Birth of Modern America: 1900-1912. † *Illus.* TB/3022

RUSSEL B. NYE: Midwestern Progressive Politics: *A Historical Study of its Origins and Development, 1870-1958* TB/1202

WALTER RAUSCHENBUSCH: Christianity and the Social Crisis. ‡ *Edited by Robert D. Cross* TB/3059

PHILIP SELZNICK: TVA and the Grass Roots: *A Study in the Sociology of Formal Organization* TB/1230

GEORGE B. TINDALL, Ed.: A Populist Reader ‡ TB/3069

TWELVE SOUTHERNERS: I'll Take My Stand: *The South and the Agrarian Tradition. Intro. by Louis D. Rubin, Jr. Biographical Essays by Virginia Rock* TB/1072

WALTER E. WEYL: The New Democracy: *An Essay on Certain Political Tendencies in the United States. ‡ Edited by Charles B. Forcey* TB/3042

Anthropology

JACQUES BARZUN: Race: *A Study in Superstition. Revised Edition* TB/1172

JOSEPH B. CASAGRANDE, Ed.: In the Company of Man: *Twenty Portraits of Anthropological Informants. Illus.* TB/3047

W. E. LE GROS CLARK: The Antecedents of Man: *Intro. to Evolution of the Primates.* ° *Illus.* TB/559

CORA DU BOIS: The People of Alor. *New Preface by the author. Illus.* Vol. I TB/1042; Vol. II TB/1043

RAYMOND FIRTH, Ed.: Man and Culture: *An Evaluation of the Work of Bronislaw Malinowski* ‖ ° TB/1133

DAVID LANDY: Tropical Childhood: *Cultural Transmission and Learning in a Rural Puerto Rican Village* ‖ TB/1235

L. S. B. LEAKEY: Adam's Ancestors: *The Evolution of Man and His Culture. Illus.* TB/1019

ROBERT H. LOWIE: Primitive Society. *Introduction by Fred Eggan* TB/1056

EDWARD BURNETT TYLOR: The Origins of Culture. *Part I of "Primitive Culture." § Intro. by Paul Radin* TB/33

EDWARD BURNETT TYLOR: Religion in Primitive Culture. *Part II of "Primitive Culture." § Intro. by Paul Radin* TB/34

W. LLOYD WARNER: A Black Civilization: *A Study of an Australian Tribe.* ‖ *Illus.* TB/3056

Art and Art History

WALTER LOWRIE: Art in the Early Church. *Revised Edition. 452 illus.* TB/124

EMILE MÂLE: The Gothic Image: *Religious Art in France of the Thirteenth Century. § 190 illus.* TB/44

MILLARD MEISS: Painting in Florence and Siena after the Black Death: *The Arts, Religion and Society in the Mid-Fourteenth Century. 169 illus.* TB/1148

ERICH NEUMANN: The Archetypal World of Henry Moore. *107 illus.* TB/2020

DORA & ERWIN PANOFSKY: Pandora's Box: *The Changing Aspects of a Mythical Symbol. Revised Edition. Illus.* TB/2021

ERWIN PANOFSKY: Studies in Iconology: *Humanistic Themes in the Art of the Renaissance. 180 illustrations* TB/1077

ALEXANDRE PIANKOFF: The Shrines of Tut-Ankh-Amon. *Edited by N. Rambova. 117 illus.* TB/2011

JEAN SEZNEC: The Survival of the Pagan Gods: *The Mythological Tradition and Its Place in Renaissance Humanism and Art. 108 illustrations* TB/2004

OTTO VON SIMSON: The Gothic Cathedral: *Origins of Gothic Architecture and the Medieval Concept of Order. 58 illus.* TB/2018

HEINRICH ZIMMER: Myths and Symbols in Indian Art and Civilization. *70 illustrations* TB/2005

Business, Economics & Economic History

REINHARD BENDIX: Work and Authority in Industry: *Ideologies of Management in the Course of Industrialization* TB/3035
GILBERT BURCK & EDITORS OF FORTUNE: The Computer Age: *And Its Potential for Management* TB/1179
THOMAS C. COCHRAN: The American Business System: *A Historical Perspective, 1900-1955* TB/1080
THOMAS C. COCHRAN: The Inner Revolution: *Essays on the Social Sciences in History* TB/1140
THOMAS C. COCHRAN & WILLIAM MILLER: The Age of Enterprise: *A Social History of Industrial America* TB/1054
ROBERT DAHL & CHARLES E. LINDBLOM: Politics, Economics, and Welfare: *Planning & Politico-Economic Systems Resolved into Basic Social Processes* TB/3037
PETER F. DRUCKER: The New Society: *The Anatomy of Industrial Order* TB/1082
EDITORS OF FORTUNE: America in the Sixties: *The Economy and the Society* TB/1015
ROBERT L. HEILBRONER: The Great Ascent: *The Struggle for Economic Development in Our Time* TB/3030
FRANK H. KNIGHT: The Economic Organization TB/1214
FRANK H. KNIGHT: Risk, Uncertainty and Profit TB/1215
ABBA P. LERNER: Everybody's Business: *Current Assumptions in Economics and Public Policy* TB/3051
ROBERT GREEN MCCLOSKEY: American Conservatism in the Age of Enterprise, 1865-1910 TB/1137
PAUL MANTOUX: The Industrial Revolution in the Eighteenth Century: *The Beginnings of the Modern Factory System in England* ° TB/1079
WILLIAM MILLER, Ed.: Men in Business: *Essays on the Historical Role of the Entrepreneur* TB/1081
RICHARD B. MORRIS: Government and Labor in Early America TB/1244
HERBERT SIMON: The Shape of Automation: *For Men and Management* TB/1245
PERRIN STRYKER: The Character of the Executive: *Eleven Studies in Managerial Qualities* TB/1041
PIERRE URI: Partnership for Progress: *A Program for Transatlantic Action* TB/3036

Contemporary Culture

JACQUES BARZUN: The House of Intellect TB/1051
JOHN U. NEF: Cultural Foundations of Industrial Civilization TB/1024
NATHAN M. PUSEY: The Age of the Scholar: *Observations on Education in a Troubled Decade* TB/1157
PAUL VALÉRY: The Outiook for Intelligence TB/2016

Historiography & Philosophy of History

JACOB BURCKHARDT: On History and Historians. *Intro. by H. R. Trevor-Roper* TB/1216
WILHELM DILTHEY: Pattern and Meaning in History: *Thoughts on History and Society. ° Edited with an Introduction by H. P. Rickman* TB/1075
J. H. HEXTER: Reappraisals in History: *New Views on History & Society in Early Modern Europe* TB/1100
H. STUART HUGHES: History as Art and as Science: *Twin Vistas on the Past* TB/1207
RAYMOND KLIBANSKY & H. J. PATON, Eds.: Philosophy and History: *The Ernst Cassirer Festschrift. Illus.* TB/1115
GEORGE H. NADEL, Ed.: Studies in the Philosophy of History: *Selected Essays from History and Theory* TB/1208
JOSE ORTEGA Y GASSET: The Modern Theme. *Introduction by Jose Ferrater Mora* TB/1038
KARL R. POPPER: The Open Society and Its Enemies
Vol. I: The Spell of Plato TB/1101
Vol. II: The High Tide of Prophecy: Hegel, Marx and the Aftermath TB/1102
KARL R. POPPER: The Poverty of Historicism ° TB/1126
G. J. RENIER: History: Its Purpose and Method TB/1209
W. H. WALSH: Philosophy of History: *An Introduction* TB/1020

History: General

L. CARRINGTON GOODRICH: A Short History of the Chinese People. *Illus.* TB/3015
DAN N. JACOBS & HANS H. BAERWALD: Chinese Communism: *Selected Documents* TB/3031
BERNARD LEWIS: The Arabs in History TB/1029

History: Ancient

A. ANDREWES: The Greek Tyrants TB/1103
ADOLF ERMAN, Ed.: The Ancient Egyptians: *A Sourcebook of Their Writings. New material and Introduction by William Kelly Simpson* TB/1233
MICHAEL GRANT: Ancient History ° TB/1190
SAMUEL NOAH KRAMER: Sumerian Mythology TB/1055
NAPHTALI LEWIS & MEYER REINHOLD, Eds.: Roman Civilization. *Sourcebook I: The Republic* TB/1231
NAPHTALI LEWIS & MEYER REINHOLD, Eds.: Roman Civilization. *Sourcebook II: The Empire* TB/1232

History: Medieval

P. BOISSONNADE: Life and Work in Medieval Europe: *The Evolution of the Medieval Economy, the 5th to the 15th Century. ° Preface by Lynn White, Jr.* TB/1141
HELEN CAM: England before Elizabeth TB/1026
NORMAN COHN: The Pursuit of the Millennium: *Revolutionary Messianism in Medieval and Reformation Europe* TB/1037
G. G. COULTON: Medieval Village, Manor, and Monastery TB/1022
HEINRICH FICHTENAU: The Carolingian Empire: *The Age of Charlemagne* TB/1142
F. L. GANSHOF: Feudalism TB/1058
EDWARD GIBBON: The Triumph of Christendom in the Roman Empire *(Chaps. XV-XX of "Decline and Fall," J. B. Bury edition). § Illus.* TB/46
W. O. HASSALL, Ed.: Medieval England: *As Viewed by Contemporaries* TB/1205
DENYS HAY: The Medieval Centuries ° TB/1192
J. M. HUSSEY: The Byzantine World TB/1057
FERDINAND LOT: The End of the Ancient World and the Beginnings of the Middle Ages. *Introduction by Glanville Downey* TB/1044
G. MOLLAT: The Popes at Avignon: 1305-1378 TB/308
CHARLES PETIT-DUTAILLIS: The Feudal Monarchy in France and England: *From the Tenth to the Thirteenth Century* ° TB/1165
HENRI PIERENNE: Early Democracies in the Low Countries: *Urban Society and Political Conflict in the Middle Ages and the Renaissance. Introduction by John H. Mundy* TB/1110
STEVEN RUNCIMAN: A History of the Crusades.
Volume I: *The First Crusade and the Foundation of the Kingdom of Jerusalem. Illus.* TB/1143
Volume II: *The Kingdom of Jerusalem and the Frankish East, 1100-1187. Illus.* TB/1243
FERDINAND SCHEVILL: Siena: *The History of a Medieval Commune. Intro. by William M. Bowsky* TB/1164
SULPICIUS SEVERUS et al.: The Western Fathers: *Being the Lives of Martin of Tours, Ambrose, Augustine of Hippo, Honoratus of Arles and Germanus of Auxerre. Edited and translated by F. R. Hoare* TB/309
HENRY OSBORN TAYLOR: The Classical Heritage of the Middle Ages. *Foreword and Biblio. by Kenneth M. Setton* TB/1117
F. VAN DER MEER: Augustine the Bishop: *Church and Society at the Dawn of the Middle Ages* TB/304
J. M. WALLACE-HADRILL: The Barbarian West: *The Early Middle Ages, A.D. 400-1000* TB/1061

History: Renaissance & Reformation

JACOB BURCKHARDT: The Civilization of the Renaissance in Italy. *Intro. by Benjamin Nelson & Charles Trinkaus. Illus.* Vol. I TB/40; Vol. II TB/41

JOHN CALVIN & JACOPO SADOLETO: A Reformation Debate. *Edited by John C. Olin* TB/1239

ERNST CASSIRER: The Individual and the Cosmos in Renaissance Philosophy. *Translated with an Introduction by Mario Domandi* TB/1097

FEDERICO CHABOD: Machiavelli and the Renaissance TB/1193

EDWARD P. CHEYNEY: The Dawn of a New Era, 1250-1453. * *Illus.* TB/3002

R. TREVOR DAVIES: The Golden Century of Spain, 1501-1621 ° TB/1194

DESIDERIUS ERASMUS: Christian Humanism and the Reformation: *Selected Writings. Edited and translated by John C. Olin* TB/1166

WALLACE K. FERGUSON et al.: Facets of the Renaissance TB/1098

WALLACE K. FERGUSON et al.: The Renaissance: *Six Essays. Illus.* TB/1084

JOHN NEVILLE FIGGIS: The Divine Right of Kings. *Introduction by G. R. Elton* TB/1191

JOHN NEVILLE FIGGIS: Political Thought from Gerson to Grotius: 1414-1625: *Seven Studies. Introduction by Garrett Mattingly* TB/1032

MYRON P. GILMORE: The World of Humanism, 1453-1517.* *Illus.* TB/3003

FRANCESCO GUICCIARDINI: Maxims and Reflections of a Renaissance Statesman *(Ricordi). Trans. by Mario Domandi. Intro. by Nicolai Rubinstein* TB/1160

J. H. HEXTER: More's Utopia: *The Biography of an Idea. New Epilogue by the Author* TB/1195

HAJO HOLBORN: Ulrich von Hutten and the German Reformation TB/1238

JOHAN HUIZINGA: Erasmus and the Age of Reformation. *Illus.* TB/19

ULRICH VON HUTTEN et al.: On the Eve of the Reformation: *"Letters of Obscure Men." Introduction by Hajo Holborn* TB/1124

PAUL O. KRISTELLER: Renaissance Thought: *The Classic, Scholastic, and Humanist Strains* TB/1048

PAUL O. KRISTELLER: Renaissance Thought II: *Papers on Humanism and the Arts* TB/1163

NICCOLÒ MACHIAVELLI: History of Florence and of the Affairs of Italy: *from the earliest times to the death of Lorenzo the Magnificent. Introduction by Felix Gilbert* TB/1027

ALFRED VON MARTIN: Sociology of the Renaissance. *Introduction by Wallace K. Ferguson* TB/1099

GARRETT MATTINGLY et al.: Renaissance Profiles. *Edited by J. H. Plumb* TB/1162

MILLARD MEISS: Painting in Florence and Siena after the Black Death: *The Arts, Religion and Society in the Mid-Fourteenth Century. 169 illus.* TB/1148

J. E. NEALE: The Age of Catherine de Medici ° TB/1085

ERWIN PANOFSKY: Studies in Iconology: *Humanistic Themes in the Art of the Renaissance. 180 illustrations* TB/1077

J. H. PARRY: The Establishment of the European Hegemony: 1415-1715: *Trade and Exploration in the Age of the Renaissance* TB/1045

J. H. PLUMB: The Italian Renaissance: *A Concise Survey of Its History and Culture* TB/1161

CECIL ROTH: The Jews in the Renaissance. *Illus.* TB/834

A. L. ROWSE: The Expansion of Elizabethan England. ° *Illus.* TB/1220

GORDON RUPP: Luther's Progress to the Diet of Worms ° TB/120

FERDINAND SCHEVILL: The Medici. *Illus.* TB/1010

FERDINAND SCHEVILL: Medieval and Renaissance Florence. *Illus.* Volume I: *Medieval Florence* TB/1090
Volume II: *The Coming of Humanism and the Age of the Medici* TB/1091

G. M. TREVELYAN: England in the Age of Wycliffe, 1368-1520 ° TB/1112

VESPASIANO: Renaissance Princes, Popes, and Prelates: *The Vespasiano Memoirs: Lives of Illustrious Men of the XVth Century. Intro. by Myron P. Gilmore* TB/1111

History: Modern European

FREDERICK B. ARTZ: Reaction and Revolution, 1815-1832. * *Illus.* TB/3034

MAX BELOFF: The Age of Absolutism, 1660-1815 TB/1062

ROBERT C. BINKLEY: Realism and Nationalism, 1852-1871. * *Illus.* TB/3038

ASA BRIGGS: The Making of Modern England, 1784-1867: *The Age of Improvement* ° TB/1203

CRANE BRINTON: A Decade of Revolution, 1789-1799. * *Illus.* TB/3018

D. W. BROGAN: The Development of Modern France. °
Volume I: *From the Fall of the Empire to the Dreyfus Affair* TB/1184
Volume II: *The Shadow of War, World War I, Between the Two Wars. New Introduction by the Author* TB/1185

J. BRONOWSKI & BRUCE MAZLISH: The Western Intellectual Tradition: *From Leonardo to Hegel* TB/3001

GEOFFREY BRUUN: Europe and the French Imperium, 1799-1814. * *Illus.* TB/3033

ALAN BULLOCK: Hitler, A Study in Tyranny. ° *Illus.* TB/1123

E. H. CARR: The Twenty Years' Crisis, 1919-1939: *An Introduction to the Study of International Relations* ° TB/1122

GORDON A. CRAIG: From Bismarck to Adenauer: *Aspects of German Statecraft. Revised Edition* TB/1171

WALTER L. DORN: Competition for Empire, 1740-1763. * *Illus.* TB/3032

FRANKLIN L. FORD: Robe and Sword: *The Regrouping of the French Aristocracy after Louis XIV* TB/1217

CARL J. FRIEDRICH: The Age of the Baroque, 1610-1660. * *Illus.* TB/3004

RENÉ FUELOEP-MILLER: The Mind and Face of Bolshevism: *An Examination of Cultural Life in Soviet Russia. New Epilogue by the Author* TB/1188

M. DOROTHY GEORGE: London Life in the Eighteenth Century TB/1182

LEO GERSHOY: From Despotism to Revolution, 1763-1789. * *Illus.* TB/3017

C. C. GILLISPIE: Genesis and Geology: *The Decades before Darwin* § TB/51

ALBERT GOODWIN: The French Revolution TB/1064

ALBERT GUERARD: France in the Classical Age: *The Life and Death of an Ideal* TB/1183

CARLTON J. H. HAYES: A Generation of Materialism, 1871-1900. * *Illus.* TB/3039

J. H. HEXTER: Reappraisals in History: *New Views on History & Society in Early Modern Europe* TB/1100

STANLEY HOFFMANN et al.: In Search of France: *The Economy, Society and Political System in the Twentieth Century* TB/1219

A. R. HUMPHREYS: The Augustan World: *Society, Thought, and Letters in 18th Century England* ° TB/1105

DAN N. JACOBS, Ed.: The New Communist Manifesto *& Related Documents. Third edition, Revised* TB/1078

HANS KOHN: The Mind of Germany: *The Education of a Nation* TB/1204

HANS KOHN, Ed.: The Mind of Modern Russia: *Historical and Political Thought of Russia's Great Age* TB/1065

FRANK E. MANUEL: The Prophets of Paris: *Turgot, Condorcet, Saint-Simon, Fourier, and Comte* TB/1218

KINGSLEY MARTIN: French Liberal Thought in the Eighteenth Century: *A Study of Political Ideas from Bayle to Condorcet* TB/1114

L. B. NAMIER: Personalities and Powers: *Selected Essays* TB/1186

L. B. NAMIER: Vanished Supremacies: *Essays on European History, 1812-1918* ° TB/1088
JOHN U. NEF: Western Civilization Since the Renaissance: *Peace, War, Industry, and the Arts* TB/1113
FREDERICK L. NUSSBAUM: The Triumph of Science and Reason, 1660-1685. * *Illus.* TB/3009
JOHN PLAMENATZ: German Marxism and Russian Communism. ° *New Preface by the Author* TB/1189
RAYMOND W. POSTGATE, Ed.: Revolution from 1789 to 1906: *Selected Documents* TB/1063
PENFIELD ROBERTS: The Quest for Security, 1715-1740. * *Illus.* TB/3016
PRISCILLA ROBERTSON: Revolutions of 1848: *A Social History* TB/1025
ALBERT SOREL: Europe Under the Old Regime. *Translated by Francis H. Herrick* TB/1121
N. N. SUKHANOV: The Russian Revolution, 1917: *Eyewitness Account. Edited by Joel Carmichael* Vol. I TB/1066; Vol. II TB/1067
A. J. P. TAYLOR: The Habsburg Monarch, 1809-1918: *A History of the Austrian Empire and Austria-Hungary* ° TB/1187
JOHN B. WOLF: The Emergence of the Great Powers, 1685-1715. * *Illus.* TB/3010
JOHN B. WOLF: France: 1814-1919: *The Rise of a Liberal-Democratic Society* TB/3019

Intellectual History & History of Ideas

HERSCHEL BAKER: The Image of Man: *A Study of the Idea of Human Dignity in Classical Antiquity, the Middle Ages, and the Renaissance* TB/1047
R. R. BOLGAR: The Classical Heritage and Its Beneficiaries: *From the Carolingian Age to the End of the Renaissance* TB/1125
RANDOLPH S. BOURNE: War and the Intellectuals: *Collected Essays, 1915-1919.* ‡ *Edited by Carl Resek* TB/3043
J. BRONOWSKI & BRUCE MAZLISH: The Western Intellectual Tradition: *From Leonardo to Hegel* TB/3001
ERNST CASSIRER: The Individual and the Cosmos in Renaissance Philosophy. *Translated with an Introduction by Mario Domandi* TB/1097
NORMAN COHN: The Pursuit of the Millennium: *Revolutionary Messianism in Medieval and Reformation Europe* TB/1037
C. C. GILLISPIE: Genesis and Geology: *The Decades before Darwin* § TB/51
G. RACHEL LEVY: Religious Conceptions of the Stone Age and Their Influence upon European Thought. *Illus. Introduction by Henri Frankfort* TB/106
ARTHUR O. LOVEJOY: The Great Chain of Being: *A Study of the History of an Idea* TB/1009
FRANK E. MANUEL: The Prophets of Paris: *Turgot, Condorcet, Saint-Simon, Fourier, and Comte* TB/1218
PERRY MILLER & T. H. JOHNSON, Editors: The Puritans: *A Sourcebook of Their Writings* Vol. I TB/1093; Vol. II TB/1094
MILTON C. NAHM: Genius and Creativity: *An Essay in the History of Ideas* TB/1196
ROBERT PAYNE: Hubris: *A Study of Pride. Foreword by Sir Herbert Read* TB/1031
RALPH BARTON PERRY: The Thought and Character of William James: *Briefer Version* TB/1156
GEORG SIMMEL et al.: Essays on Sociology, Philosophy, and Aesthetics. || *Edited by Kurt H. Wolff* TB/1234
BRUNO SNELL: The Discovery of the Mind: *The Greek Origins of European Thought* TB/1018
PAGET TOYNBEE: Dante Alighieri: *His Life and Works. Edited with Intro. by Charles S. Singleton* TB/1206
ERNEST LEE TUVESON: Millennium and Utopia: *A Study in the Background of the Idea of Progress.* || *New Preface by the Author* TB/1134
PAUL VALÉRY: The Outlook for Intelligence TB/2016
PHILIP P. WIENER: Evolution and the Founders of Pragmatism. *Foreword by John Dewey* TB/1212

Literature, Poetry, The Novel & Criticism

JAMES BAIRD: Ishmael: *The Art of Melville in the Contexts of International Primitivism* TB/1023
JACQUES BARZUN: The House of Intellect TB/1051
W. J. BATE: From Classic to Romantic: *Premises of Taste in Eighteenth Century England* TB/1036
RACHEL BESPALOFF: On the Iliad TB/2006
R. P. BLACKMUR et al.: Lectures in Criticism. *Introduction by Huntington Cairns* TB/2003
ABRAHAM CAHAN: The Rise of David Levinsky: *a documentary novel of social mobility in early twentieth century America. Intro. by John Higham* TB/1028
ERNST R. CURTIUS: European Literature and the Latin Middle Ages TB/2015
GEORGE ELIOT: Daniel Deronda: *a novel. Introduction by F. R. Leavis* TB/1039
ADOLF ERMAN, Ed.: The Ancient Egyptians: *A Sourcebook of Their Writings. New Material and Introduction by William Kelly Simpson* TB/1233
ÉTIENNE GILSON: Dante and Philosophy TB/1089
ALFRED HARBAGE: As They Liked It: *A Study of Shakespeare's Moral Artistry* TB/1035
STANLEY R. HOPPER, Ed.: Spiritual Problems in Contemporary Literature § TB/21
A. R. HUMPHREYS: The Augustan World: *Society, Thought and Letters in 18th Century England* ° TB/1105
ALDOUS HUXLEY: Antic Hay & The Giaconda Smile. ° *Introduction by Martin Green* TB/3503
ALDOUS HUXLEY: Brave New World & Brave New World Revisited. ° *Introduction by Martin Green* TB/3501
HENRY JAMES: Roderick Hudson: *a novel. Introduction by Leon Edel* TB/1016
HENRY JAMES: The Tragic Muse: *a novel. Introduction by Leon Edel* TB/1017
ARNOLD KETTLE: An Introduction to the English Novel. Volume I: *Defoe to George Eliot* TB/1011
Volume II: *Henry James to the Present* TB/1012
ROGER SHERMAN LOOMIS: The Development of Arthurian Romance TB/1167
JOHN STUART MILL: On Bentham and Coleridge. *Introduction by F. R. Leavis* TB/1070
KENNETH B. MURDOCK: Literature and Theology in Colonial New England TB/99
SAMUEL PEPYS: The Diary of Samuel Pepys. ° *Edited by O. F. Morshead. Illus. by Ernest Shepard* TB/1007
ST.-JOHN PERSE: Seamarks TB/2002
GEORGE SANTAYANA: Interpretations of Poetry and Religion § TB/9
HEINRICH STRAUMANN: American Literature in the Twentieth Century. *Third Edition, Revised* TB/1168
PAGET TOYNBEE: Dante Alighieri: *His Life and Works. Edited with Intro. by Charles S. Singleton* TB/1206
DOROTHY VAN GHENT: The English Novel: *Form and Function* TB/1050
E. B. WHITE: One Man's Meat. *Introduction by Walter Blair* TB/3505
MORTON DAUWEN ZABEL, Editor: Literary Opinion in America Vol. I TB/3013; Vol. II TB/3014

Myth, Symbol & Folklore

JOSEPH CAMPBELL, Editor: Pagan and Christian Mysteries. *Illus.* TB/2013
MIRCEA ELIADE: Cosmos and History: *The Myth of the Eternal Return* § TB/2050
MERCEA ELIADE: Rites and Symbols of Initiation: *The Mysteries of Birth and Rebirth* § TB/1236
C. G. JUNG & C. KERÉNYI: Essays on a Science of Mythology: *The Myths of the Divine Child and the Divine Maiden* TB/2014
DORA & ERWIN PANOFSKY: Pandora's Box: *The Changing Aspects of a Mythical Symbol. Revised Edition. Illus.* TB/2021

ERWIN PANOFSKY: Studies in Iconology: *Humanistic Themes in the Art of the Renaissance. 180 illustrations* TB/1077

JEAN SEZNEC: The Survival of the Pagan Gods: *The Mythological Tradition and its Place in Renaissance Humanism and Art. 108 illustrations* TB/2004

HELLMUT WILHELM: Change: *Eight Lectures on the I Ching* TB/2019

HEINRICH ZIMMER: Myths and Symbols in Indian Art and Civilization. *70 illustrations* TB/2005

Philosophy

G. E. M. ANSCOMBE: An Introduction to Wittgenstein's Tractatus. *Second edition, Revised.* ° TB/1210

HENRI BERGSON: Time and Free Will: *An Essay on the Immediate Data of Consciousness* ° TB/1021

H. J. BLACKHAM: Six Existentialist Thinkers: *Kierkegaard, Nietzsche, Jaspers, Marcel, Heidegger, Sartre* ° TB/1002

CRANE BRINTON: Nietzsche. *New Preface, Bibliography and Epilogue by the Author* TB/1197

ERNST CASSIRER: The Individual and the Cosmos in Renaissance Philosophy. *Translated with an Introduction by Mario Domandi* TB/1097

ERNST CASSIRER: Rousseau, Kant and Goethe. *Introduction by Peter Gay* TB/1092

FREDERICK COPLESTON: Medieval Philosophy ° TB/376

F. M. CORNFORD: Principium Sapientiae: *A Study of the Origins of Greek Philosophical Thought. Edited by W. K. C. Guthrie* TB/1213

F. M. CORNFORD: From Religion to Philosophy: *A Study in the Origins of Western Speculation* § TB/20

WILFRID DESAN: The Tragic Finale: *An Essay on the Philosophy of Jean-Paul Sartre* TB/1030

A. P. D'ENTRÈVES: Natural Law: *An Historical Survey* TB/1223

HERBERT FINGARETTE: The Self in Transformation: *Psychoanalysis, Philosophy and the Life of the Spirit* || TB/1177

PAUL FRIEDLÄNDER: Plato: *An Introduction* TB/2017

ÉTIENNE GILSON: Dante and Philosophy TB/1089

WILLIAM CHASE GREENE: Moira: *Fate, Good, and Evil in Greek Thought* TB/1104

W. K. C. GUTHRIE: The Greek Philosophers: *From Thales to Aristotle* ° TB/1008

F. H. HEINEMANN: Existentialism and the Modern Predicament TB/28

ISAAC HUSIK: A History of Medieval Jewish Philosophy JP/3

EDMUND HUSSERL: Phenomenology and the Crisis of Philosophy. *Translated with an Introduction by Quentin Lauer* TB/1170

IMMANUEL KANT: The Doctrine of Virtue, *being Part II of* The Metaphysic of Morals. *Trans. with Notes & Intro. by Mary J. Gregor. Foreword by H. J. Paton* TB/110

IMMANUEL KANT: Groundwork of the Metaphysic of Morals. *Trans. & analyzed by H. J. Paton* TB/1159

IMMANUEL KANT: Lectures on Ethics. § *Introduction by Lewis W. Beck* TB/105

IMMANUEL KANT: Religion Within the Limits of Reason Alone. § *Intro. by T. M. Greene & J. Silber* TB/67

QUENTIN LAUER: Phenomenology: *Its Genesis and Prospect* TB/1169

GABRIEL MARCEL: Being and Having: *An Existential Diary. Intro. by James Collins* TB/310

GEORGE A. MORGAN: What Nietzsche Means TB/1198

PHILO, SAADYA GAON, & JEHUDA HALEVI: Three Jewish Philosophers. *Ed. by Hans Lewy, Alexander Altmann, & Isaak Heinemann* TB/813

MICHAEL POLANYI: Personal Knowledge: *Towards a Post-Critical Philosophy* TB/1158

WILLARD VAN ORMAN QUINE: Elementary Logic: *Revised Edition* TB/577

WILLARD VAN ORMAN QUINE: From a Logical Point of View: *Logico-Philosophical Essays* TB/566

BERTRAND RUSSELL et al.: The Philosophy of Bertrand Russell. *Edited by Paul Arthur Schilpp*
Vol. I TB/1095; Vol. II TB/1096

L. S. STEBBING: A Modern Introduction to Logic TB/538

ALFRED NORTH WHITEHEAD: Process and Reality: *An Essay in Cosmology* TB/1033

PHILIP P. WIENER: Evolution and the Founders of Pragmatism. *Foreword by John Dewey* TB/1212

WILHELM WINDELBAND: A History of Philosophy
Vol. I: *Greek, Roman, Medieval* TB/38
Vol. II: *Renaissance, Enlightenment, Modern* TB/39

LUDWIG WITTGENSTEIN: The Blue and Brown Books ° TB/1211

Political Science & Government

JEREMY BENTHAM: The Handbook of Political Fallacies. *Introduction by Crane Brinton* TB/1069

KENNETH E. BOULDING: Conflict and Defense: *A General Theory* TB/3024

CRANE BRINTON: English Political Thought in the Nineteenth Century TB/1071

EDWARD S. CORWIN: American Constitutional History: *Essays edited by Alpheus T. Mason and Gerald Garvey* TB/1136

ROBERT DAHL & CHARLES E. LINDBLOM: Politics, Economics, and Welfare: *Planning and Politico-Economic Systems Resolved into Basic Social Processes* TB/3037

JOHN NEVILLE FIGGIS: The Divine Right of Kings. *Introduction by G. R. Elton* TB/1191

JOHN NEVILLE FIGGIS: Political Thought from Gerson to Grotius: 1414-1625: *Seven Studies. Introduction by Garrett Mattingly* TB/1032

F. L. GANSHOF: Feudalism TB/1058

G. P. GOOCH: English Democratic Ideas in Seventeenth Century TB/1006

J. H. HEXTER: More's Utopia: *The Biography of an Idea. New Epilogue by the Author* TB/1195

SIDNEY HOOK: Reason, Social Myths and Democracy TB/1237

ROBERT H. JACKSON: The Supreme Court in the American System of Government TB/1106

DAN N. JACOBS, Ed.: The New Communist Manifesto & *Related Documents. Third edition, Revised* TB/1078

DAN N. JACOBS & HANS BAERWALD, Eds.: Chinese Communism: *Selected Documents* TB/3031

ROBERT GREEN MCCLOSKEY: American Conservatism in the Age of Enterprise, 1865-1910 TB/1137

KINGSLEY MARTIN: French Liberal Thought in the Eighteenth Century: *Political Ideas from Bayle to Condorcet* TB/1114

ROBERTO MICHELS: First Lectures in Political Sociology. *Edited by Alfred De Grazia* || ° TB/1224

JOHN STUART MILL: On Bentham and Coleridge. *Introduction by F. R. Leavis* TB/1070

BARRINGTON MOORE, JR.: Political Power and Social Theory: *Seven Studies* || TB/1221

BARRINGTON MOORE, JR.: Soviet Politics—The Dilemma of Power: *The Role of Ideas in Social Change* || TB/1222

JOHN B. MORRALL: Political Thought in Medieval Times TB/1076

JOHN PLAMENATZ: German Marxism and Russian Communism. ° *New Preface by the Author* TB/1189

KARL R. POPPER: The Open Society and Its Enemies
Vol. I: *The Spell of Plato* TB/1101
Vol. II: *The High Tide of Prophecy: Hegel, Marx, and the Aftermath* TB/1102

HENRI DE SAINT-SIMON: Social Organization, The Science of Man, and Other Writings. *Edited and Translated by Felix Markham* TB/1152

JOSEPH A. SCHUMPETER: Capitalism, Socialism and Democracy TB/3008

CHARLES H. SHINN: Mining Camps: *A Study in American Frontier Government.* ‡ *Edited by Rodman W. Paul* TB/3062

Psychology

ALFRED ADLER: The Individual Psychology of Alfred Adler. *Edited by Heinz L. and Rowena R. Ansbacher* TB/1154

ALFRED ADLER: Problems of Neurosis. *Introduction by Heinz L. Ansbacher* TB/1145

ANTON T. BOISEN: The Exploration of the Inner World: *A Study of Mental Disorder and Religious Experience* TB/87

HERBERT FINGARETTE: The Self in Transformation: *Psychoanalysis, Philosophy and the Life of the Spirit* || TB/1177

SIGMUND FREUD: On Creativity and the Unconscious: *Papers on the Psychology of Art, Literature, Love, Religion.* § *Intro. by Benjamin Nelson* TB/45

C. JUDSON HERRICK: The Evolution of Human Nature TB/545

WILLIAM JAMES: Psychology: *The Briefer Course. Edited with an Intro. by Gordon Allport* TB/1034

C. G. JUNG: Psychological Reflections TB/2001

C. G. JUNG: Symbols of Transformation: *An Analysis of the Prelude to a Case of Schizophrenia. Illus.* Vol. I: TB/2009; Vol. II TB/2010

C. G. JUNG & C. KERÉNYI: Essays on a Science of Mythology: *The Myths of the Divine Child and the Divine Maiden* TB/2014

JOHN T. MC NEILL: A History of the Cure of Souls TB/126

KARL MENNINGER: Theory of Psychoanalytic Technique TB/1144

ERICH NEUMANN: Amor and Psyche: *The Psychic Development of the Feminine* TB/2012

ERICH NEUMANN: The Archetypal World of Henry Moore. *107 illus.* TB/2020

ERICH NEUMANN: The Origins and History of Consciousness Vol. I *Illus.* TB/2007; Vol. II TB/2008

C. P. OBERNDORF: A History of Psychoanalysis in America TB/1147

RALPH BARTON PERRY: The Thought and Character of William James: *Briefer Version* TB/1156

JEAN PIAGET, BÄRBEL INHELDER, & ALINA SZEMINSKA: The Child's Conception of Geometry ° TB/1146

JOHN H. SCHAAR: Escape from Authority: *The Perspectives of Erich Fromm* TB/1155

Sociology

JACQUES BARZUN: Race: *A Study in Superstition. Revised Edition* TB/1172

BERNARD BERELSON, Ed.: The Behavioral Sciences Today TB/1127

ABRAHAM CAHAN: The Rise of David Levinsky: *A documentary novel of social mobility in early twentieth century America. Intro. by John Higham* TB/1028

THOMAS C. COCHRAN: The Inner Revolution: *Essays on the Social Sciences in History* TB/1140

ALLISON DAVIS & JOHN DOLLARD: Children of Bondage: *The Personality Development of Negro Youth in the Urban South* || TB/3049

ST. CLAIR DRAKE & HORACE R. CAYTON: Black Metropolis: *A Study of Negro Life in a Northern City. Revised and Enlarged. Intro. by Everett C. Hughes* Vol. I TB/1086; Vol. II TB/1087

EMILE DURKHEIM et al.: Essays on Sociology and Philosophy: *With Analyses of Durkheim's Life and Work.* || *Edited by Kurt H. Wolff* TB/1151

LEON FESTINGER, HENRY W. RIECKEN & STANLEY SCHACHTER: When Prophecy Fails: *A Social and Psychological Account of a Modern Group that Predicted the Destruction of the World* || TB/1132

ALVIN W. GOULDNER: Wildcat Strike: *A Study in Worker-Management Relationships* || TB/1176

FRANCIS J. GRUND: Aristocracy in America: *Social Class in the Formative Years of the New Nation* TB/1001

KURT LEWIN: Field Theory in Social Science: *Selected Theoretical Papers.* || *Edited with a Foreword by* Dorwin Cartwright TB/1135

R. M. MAC IVER: Social Causation TB/1153

ROBERT K. MERTON, LEONARD BROOM, LEONARD S. COTTRELL, JR., Editors: Sociology Today: *Problems and Prospects* || Vol. I TB/1173; Vol. II TB/1174

ROBERTO MICHELS: First Lectures in Political Sociology. *Edited by Alfred De Grazia* || ° TB/1224

BARRINGTON MOORE, JR.: Political Power and Social Theory: *Seven Studies* || TB/1221

BARRINGTON MOORE, JR.: Soviet Politics—The Dilemma of Power: *The Role of Ideas in Social Change* || TB/1222

TALCOTT PARSONS & EDWARD A. SHILS, Editors: Toward a General Theory of Action: *Theoretical Foundations for the Social Sciences* TB/1083

JOHN H. ROHRER & MUNRO S. EDMONSON, Eds.: The Eighth Generation Grows Up: *Cultures and Personalities of New Orleans Negroes* || TB/3050

ARNOLD ROSE: The Negro in America: *The Condensed Version of Gunnar Myrdal's* An American Dilemma TB/3048

KURT SAMUELSSON: Religion and Economic Action: *A Critique of Max Weber's* The Protestant Ethic and the Spirit of Capitalism. || ° *Trans. by E. G. French. Ed. with Intro. by D. C. Coleman* TB/1131

PHILIP SELZNICK: TVA and the Grass Roots: *A Study in the Sociology of Formal Organization* TB/1230

GEORG SIMMEL et al.: Essays on Sociology, Philosophy, and Aesthetics. || *Edited by Kurt H. Wolff* TB/1234

HERBERT SIMON: The Shape of Automation: *For Men and Management* TB/1245

PITIRIM A. SOROKIN: Contemporary Sociological Theories. *Through the First Quarter of the 20th Century* TB/3046

MAURICE R. STEIN: The Eclipse of Community: *An Interpretation of American Studies* TB/1128

FERDINAND TÖNNIES: Community and Society: *Gemeinschaft und Gesellschaft. Translated and edited by Charles P. Loomis* TB/1116

W. LLOYD WARNER & Associates: Democracy in Jonesville: *A Study in Quality and Inequality* TB/1129

W. LLOYD WARNER: Social Class in America: *The Evaluation of Status* TB/1013

RELIGION

Ancient & Classical

J. H. BREASTED: Development of Religion and Thought in Ancient Egypt. *Introduction by John A. Wilson* TB/57

HENRI FRANKFORT: Ancient Egyptian Religion: *An Interpretation* TB/77

G. RACHEL LEVY: Religious Conceptions of the Stone Age *and their Influence upon European Thought. Illus. Introduction by Henri Frankfort* TB/106

MARTIN P. NILSSON: Greek Folk Religion. *Foreword by Arthur Darby Nock* TB/78

ALEXANDRE PIANKOFF: The Shrines of Tut-Ankh-Amon. *Edited by N. Rambova. 117 illus.* TB/2011

H. J. ROSE: Religion in Greece and Rome TB/55

Biblical Thought & Literature

W. F. ALBRIGHT: The Biblical Period from Abraham to Ezra TB/102

C. K. BARRETT, Ed.: The New Testament Background: *Selected Documents* TB/86

C. H. DODD: The Authority of the Bible TB/43

M. S. ENSLIN: Christian Beginnings TB/5

M. S. ENSLIN: The Literature of the Christian Movement TB/6

JOHN GRAY: Archaeology and the Old Testament World. *Illus.* TB/127
JAMES MUILENBURG: The Way of Israel: *Biblical Faith and Ethics* TB/133
H. H. ROWLEY: The Growth of the Old Testament TB/107
D. WINTON THOMAS, Ed.: Documents from Old Testament Times TB/85

The Judaic Tradition

LEO BAECK: Judaism and Christianity. *Trans. with Intro. by Walter Kaufmann* JP/23
SALO W. BARON: Modern Nationalism and Religion JP/18
MARTIN BUBER: Eclipse of God: *Studies in the Relation Between Religion and Philosophy* TB/12
MARTIN BUBER: The Knowledge of Man: *Selected Essays. Edited with an Introduction by Maurice Friedman. Translated by Maurice Friedman and Ronald Gregor Smith* TB/135
MARTIN BUBER: Moses: *The Revelation and the Covenant* TB/27
MARTIN BUBER: Pointing the Way. *Introduction by Maurice S. Friedman* TB/103
MARTIN BUBER: The Prophetic Faith TB/73
MARTIN BUBER: Two Types of Faith: *the interpenetration of Judaism and Christianity* ° TB/75
ERNST LUDWIG EHRLICH: A Concise History of Israel: *From the Earliest Times to the Destruction of the Temple in A.D. 70* ° TB/128
MAURICE S. FRIEDMAN: Martin Buber: *The Life of Dialogue* TB/64
LOUIS GINZBERG: Students, Scholars and Saints JP/2
SOLOMON GRAYZEL: A History of the Contemporary Jews TB/816
WILL HERBERG: Judaism and Modern Man TB/810
ABRAHAM J. HESCHEL: God in Search of Man: *A Philosophy of Judaism* JP/7
ISAAC HUSIK: A History of Medieval Jewish Philosophy JP/3
FLAVIUS JOSEPHUS: The Great Roman-Jewish War, *with* The Life of Josephus. *Introduction by William R. Farmer* TB/74
JACOB R. MARCUS The Jew in the Medieval World TB/814
MAX L. MARGOLIS & ALEXANDER MARX: A History of the Jewish People TB/806
T. J. MEEK: Hebrew Origins TB/69
C. G. MONTEFIORE & H. LOEWE, Eds.: A Rabbinic Anthology. JP/32
JAMES PARKES: The Conflict of the Church and the Synagogue: *The Jews and Early Christianity* JP/21
PHILO, SAADYA GAON, & JEHUDA HALEVI: Three Jewish Philosophers. *Ed. by Hans Lewey, Alexander Altmann, & Isaak Heinemann* TB/813
HERMAN L. STRACK: Introduction to the Talmud and Midrash TB/808
JOSHUA TRACHTENBERG: The Devil and the Jews: *The Medieval Conception of the Jew and its Relation to Modern Anti-Semitism* JP/22

Christianity: General

ROLAND H. BAINTON: Christendom: *A Short History of Christianity and its Impact on Western Civilization. Illus.* Vol. I TB/131; Vol. II TB/132

Christianity: Origins & Early Development

AUGUSTINE: An Augustine Synthesis. *Edited by Erich Przywara* TB/335
ADOLF DEISSMANN: Paul: *A Study in Social and Religious History* TB/15
EDWARD GIBBON: The Triumph of Christendom in the Roman Empire *(Chaps. XV-XX of "Decline and Fall," J. B. Bury edition). § Illus.* TB/46
MAURICE GOGUEL: Jesus and the Origins of Christianity. ° *Introduction by C. Leslie Mitton*
Volume I: *Prolegomena to the Life of Jesus* TB/65
Volume II: *The Life of Jesus* TB/66
EDGAR J. GOODSPEED: A Life of Jesus TB/1
ADOLF HARNACK: The Mission and Expansion of Christianity *in the First Three Centuries. Introduction by Jaroslav Pelikan* TB/92
R. K. HARRISON: The Dead Sea Scrolls: *An Introduction* ° TB/84
EDWIN HATCH: The Influence of Greek Ideas on Christianity. *§ Introduction and Bibliography by Frederick C. Grant* TB/18
ARTHUR DARBY NOCK: Early Gentile Christianity and Its Hellenistic Background TB/111
ARTHUR DARBY NOCK: St. Paul ° TB/104
ORIGEN: On First Principles. *Edited by G. W. Butterworth. Introduction by Henri de Lubac* TB/310
JAMES PARKES: The Conflict of the Church and the Synagogue: *The Jews and Early Christianity* JP/21
SULPICIUS SEVERUS et al.: The Western Fathers: *Being the Lives of Martin of Tours, Ambrose, Augustine of Hippo, Honoratus of Arles and Germanus of Auxerre. Edited and translated by F. R. Hoare* TB/309
F. VAN DER MEER: Augustine the Bishop: *Church and Society at the Dawn of the Middle Ages* TB/304
JOHANNES WEISS: Earliest Christianity: *A History of the Period A.D. 30-150. Introduction and Bibliography by Frederick C. Grant* Volume I TB/53; Volume II TB/54

Christianity: The Middle Ages and The Reformation

JOHN CALVIN & JACOPO SADOLETO: A Reformation Debate. *Edited by John C. Olin* TB/1239
JOHANNES ECKHART: Meister Eckhart: *A Modern Translation by R. B. Blakney* TB/8
DESIDERIUS ERASMUS: Christian Humanism and the Reformation: *Selected Writings. Edited and translated by John C. Olin* TB/1166
ÉTIENNE GILSON: Dante and Philosophy TB/1089
WILLIAM HALLER: The Rise of Puritanism TB/22
HAJO HOLBORN: Ulrich von Hutten and the German Reformation TB/1238
JOHAN HUIZINGA: Erasmus and the Age of Reformation. *Illus.* TB/19
A. C. MCGIFFERT: Protestant Thought Before Kant. *Preface by Jaroslav Pelikan* TB/93
JOHN T. MCNEILL: Makers of the Christian Tradition: *From Alfred the Great to Schleiermacher* TB/121
G. MOLLAT: The Popes at Avignon, 1305-1378 TB/308
GORDON RUPP: Luther's Progress to the Diet of Worms ° TB/120

Christianity: The Protestant Tradition

KARL BARTH: Church Dogmatics: *A Selection* TB/95
KARL BARTH: Dogmatics in Outline TB/56
KARL BARTH: The Word of God and the Word of Man TB/13
RUDOLF BULTMANN et al.: Translating Theology into the Modern Age: *Historical, Systematic and Pastoral Reflections on Theology and the Church in the Contemporary Situation. Volume 2 of* Journal for Theology and the Church, *edited by Robert W. Funk in association with Gerhard Ebeling* TB/252
WINTHROP HUDSON: The Great Tradition of the American Churches TB/98
SOREN KIERKEGAARD: Edifying Discourses. *Edited with an Introduction by Paul Holmer* TB/32
SOREN KIERKEGAARD: The Journals of Kierkegaard. ° *Edited with an Introduction by Alexander Dru* TB/52
SOREN KIERKEGAARD: The Point of View for My Work as an Author: *A Report to History. § Preface by Benjamin Nelson* TB/88

SOREN KIERKEGAARD: The Present Age. § *Translated and edited by Alexander Dru. Introduction by Walter Kaufmann* TB/94
SOREN KIERKEGAARD: Purity of Heart TB/4
SOREN KIERKEGAARD: Repetition: *An Essay in Experimental Psychology. Translated with Introduction & Notes by Walter Lowrie* TB/117
SOREN KIERKEGAARD: Works of Love: *Some Christian Reflections in the Form of Discourses* TB/122
WALTER LOWRIE: Kierkegaard: *A Life* Vol. I TB/89; Vol. II TB/90
JOHN MACQUARRIE: The Scope of Demythologizing: *Bultmann and his Critics* TB/134
PERRY MILLER & T. H. JOHNSON, Editors: The Puritans: *A Sourcebook of Their Writings* Vol. I TB/1093; Vol. II TB/1094
JAMES M. ROBINSON et al.: The Bultmann School of Biblical Interpretation: New Directions? *Volume 1 of* Journal of Theology and the Church, *edited by Robert W. Funk in association with Gerhard Ebeling* TB/251
F. SCHLEIERMACHER: The Christian Faith. *Introduction by Richard R. Niebuhr* Vol. I TB/108; Vol. II TB/109
F. SCHLEIERMACHER: On Religion: *Speeches to Its Cultured Despisers. Intro. by Rudolf Otto* TB/36
PAUL TILLICH: Dynamics of Faith TB/42
EVELYN UNDERHILL: Worship TB/10
G. VAN DER LEEUW: Religion in Essence and Manifestation: *A Study in Phenomenology. Appendices by Hans H. Penner* Vol. I TB/100; Vol. II TB/101

Christianity: The Roman and Eastern Traditions

DOM CUTHBERT BUTLER: Western Mysticism: *The Teaching of Augustine, Gregory and Bernard on Contemplation and the Contemplative Life* § ° TB/312
A. ROBERT CAPONIGRI, Ed.: Modern Catholic Thinkers I: *God and Man* TB/306
A. ROBERT CAPONIGRI, Ed.: Modern Catholic Thinkers II: *The Church and the Political Order* TB/307
THOMAS CORBISHLEY, S. J.: Roman Catholicism TB/112
CHRISTOPHER DAWSON: The Historic Reality of Christian Culture TB/305
G. P. FEDOTOV: The Russian Religious Mind: *Kievan Christianity, the 10th to the 13th Centuries* TB/70
G. P. FEDOTOV, Ed.: A Treasury of Russian Spirituality TB/303
DAVID KNOWLES: The English Mystical Tradition TB/302
GABRIEL MARCEL: Being and Having: *An Existential Diary. Introduction by James Collins* TB/310
GABRIEL MARCEL: Homo Viator: *Introduction to a Metaphysic of Hope* TB/397
GUSTAVE WEIGEL, S. J.: Catholic Theology in Dialogue TB/301

Oriental Religions: Far Eastern, Near Eastern

TOR ANDRAE: Mohammed: *The Man and His Faith* TB/62
EDWARD CONZE: Buddhism: *Its Essence and Development.* ° *Foreword by Arthur Waley* TB/58
EDWARD CONZE et al., Editors: Buddhist Texts Through the Ages TB/113
ANANDA COOMARASWAMY: Buddha and the Gospel of Buddhism. *Illus.* TB/119
H. G. CREEL: Confucius and the Chinese Way TB/63
FRANKLIN EDGERTON, Trans. & Ed.: The Bhagavad Gita TB/115
SWAMI NIKHILANANDA, Trans. & Ed.: The Upanishads: *A One-Volume Abridgment* TB/114
HELLMUT WILHELM: Change: *Eight Lectures on the* I Ching TB/2019

Philosophy of Religion

NICOLAS BERDYAEV: The Beginning and the End § TB/14
NICOLAS BERDYAEV: Christian Existentialism: *A Berdyaev Synthesis. Ed. by Donald A. Lowrie* TB/130
NICOLAS BERDYAEV: The Destiny of Man TB/61
RUDOLF BULTMANN: History and Eschatology: *The Presence of Eternity* ° TB/91
RUDOLF BULTMANN AND FIVE CRITICS: Kerygma and Myth: *A Theological Debate* TB/80
RUDOLF BULTMANN and KARL KUNDSIN: Form Criticism: *Two Essays on New Testament Research. Translated by Frederick C. Grant* TB/96
MIRCEA ELIADE: The Sacred and the Profane TB/81
LUDWIG FEUERBACH: The Essence of Christianity. § *Introduction by Karl Barth. Foreword by H. Richard Niebuhr* TB/11
ADOLF HARNACK: What is Christianity? § *Introduction by Rudolf Bultmann* TB/17
FRIEDRICH HEGEL: On Christianity: *Early Theological Writings. Ed. by R. Kroner & T. M. Knox* TB/79
KARL HEIM: Christian Faith and Natural Science TB/16
IMMANUEL KANT: Religion Within the Limits of Reason Alone. § *Intro. by T. M. Greene & J. Silber* TB/67
JOHN MACQUARRIE: An Existentialist Theology: *A Comparison of Heidegger and Bultmann.* ° *Preface by Rudolf Bultmann* TB/125
PAUL RAMSEY, Ed.: Faith and Ethics: *The Theology of H. Richard Niebuhr* TB/129
PIERRE TEILHARD DE CHARDIN: The Divine Milieu ° TB/384
PIERRE TEILHARD DE CHARDIN: The Phenomenon of Man ° TB/83

Religion, Culture & Society

JOSEPH L. BLAU, Ed.: Cornerstones of Religious Freedom in America: *Selected Basic Documents, Court Decisions and Public Statements. Revised and Enlarged Edition* TB/118
C. C. GILLISPIE: Genesis and Geology: *The Decades before Darwin* § TB/51
KYLE HASELDEN: The Racial Problem in Christian Perspective TB/116
WALTER KAUFMANN, Ed.: Religion from Tolstoy to Camus: *Basic Writings on Religious Truth and Morals. Enlarged Edition* TB/123
JOHN T. MCNEILL: A History of the Cure of Souls TB/126
KENNETH B. MURDOCK: Literature and Theology in Colonial New England TB/99
H. RICHARD NIEBUHR: Christ and Culture TB/3
H. RICHARD NIEBUHR: The Kingdom of God in America TB/49
RALPH BARTON PERRY: Puritanism and Democracy TB/1138
PAUL PFUETZE: Self, Society, Existence: *Human Nature and Dialogue in the Thought of George Herbert Mead and Martin Buber* TB/1059
WALTER RAUSCHENBUSCH: Christianity and the Social Crisis. ‡ *Edited by Robert D. Cross* TB/3059
KURT SAMUELSSON: Religion and Economic Action: *A Critique of Max Weber's* The rotestant Ethic and the Spirit of Capitalism. ‖ ° *Trans. by E. G. French. Ed. with Intro. by D. C. Coleman* TB/1131
TIMOTHY L. SMITH: Revivalism and Social Reform: *Protestantism on the Eve of the Civil War* TB/1229
ERNST TROELTSCH: The Social Teaching of the Christian Churches ° Vol. I TB/71; Vol. II TB/72

NATURAL SCIENCES AND MATHEMATICS

Biological Sciences

CHARLOTTE AUERBACH: The Science of Genetics Σ TB/568
MARSTON BATES: The Natural History of Mosquitoes. *Illus.* TB/578
A. BELLAIRS: Reptiles: *Life History, Evolution, and Structure. Illus.* TB/520

LUDWIG VON BERTALANFFY: Modern Theories of Development: *An Introduction to Theoretical Biology* TB/554
LUDWIG VON BERTALANFFY: Problems of Life: *An Evaluation of Modern Biological and Scientific Thought* TB/521
HAROLD F. BLUM: Time's Arrow and Evolution TB/555
JOHN TYLER BONNER: The Ideas of Biology. Σ *Illus.* TB/570
A. J. CAIN: Animal Species and their Evolution. *Illus.* TB/519
WALTER B. CANNON: Bodily Changes in Pain, Hunger, Fear and Rage. *Illus.* TB/562
W. E. LE GROS CLARK: The Antecedents of Man: *Intro. to Evolution of the Primates.* ° *Illus.* TB/559
W. H. DOWDESWELL: Animal Ecology. *Illus.* TB/543
W. H. DOWDESWELL: The Mechanism of Evolution. *Illus.* TB/527
R. W. GERARD: Unresting Cells. *Illus.* TB/541
DAVID LACK: Darwin's Finches. *Illus.* TB/544
J. E. MORTON: Molluscs: *An Introduction to their Form and Functions. Illus.* TB/529
ADOLF PORTMANN: Animals as Social Beings. ° *Illus.* TB/572
O. W. RICHARDS: The Social Insects. *Illus.* TB/542
P. M. SHEPPARD: Natural Selection and Heredity. *Illus.* TB/528
EDMUND W. SINNOTT: Cell and Psyche: *The Biology of Purpose* TB/546
C. H. WADDINGTON: How Animals Develop. *Illus.* TB/553
C. H. WADDINGTON: The Nature of Life: *The Main Problems and Trends in Modern Biology* TB/580

Chemistry

J. R. PARTINGTON: A Short History of Chemistry. *Illus.* TB/522
J. READ: A Direct Entry to Organic Chemistry. *Illus.* TB/523
J. READ: Through Alchemy to Chemistry. *Illus.* TB/561

Communication Theory

J. R. PIERCE: Symbols, Signals and Noise: *The Nature and Process of Communication* TB/574

Geography

R. E. COKER: This Great and Wide Sea: *An Introduction to Oceanography and Marine Biology. Illus.* TB/551
F. K. HARE: The Restless Atmosphere TB/560

History of Science

W. DAMPIER, Ed.: Readings in the Literature of Science. *Illus.* TB/512
A. HUNTER DUPREE: Science in the Federal Government: *A History of Policies and Activities to 1940* TB/573
ALEXANDRE KOYRÉ: From the Closed World to the Infinite Universe: *Copernicus, Kepler, Galileo, Newton, etc.* TB/31
A. G. VAN MELSEN: From Atomos to Atom: *A History of the Concept* Atom TB/517
O. NEUGEBAUER: The Exact Sciences in Antiquity TB/552
H. T. PLEDGE: Science Since 1500: *A Short History of Mathematics, Physics, Chemistry and Biology. Illus.* TB/506
HANS THIRRING: Energy for Man: *From Windmills to Nuclear Power* TB/556
LANCELOT LAW WHYTE: Essay on Atomism: *From Democritus to 1960* TB/565
A. WOLF: A History of Science, Technology and Philosophy in the 16th and 17th Centuries. ° *Illus.* Vol. I TB/508; Vol. II TB/509
A. WOLF: A History of Science, Technology, and Philosophy in the Eighteenth Century. ° *Illus.* Vol. I TB/539; Vol. II TB/540

Mathematics

E. W. BETH: The Foundations of Mathematics: *A Study in the Philosophy of Science* TB/581
H. DAVENPORT: The Higher Arithmetic: *An Introduction to the Theory of Numbers* TB/526
H. G. FORDER: Geometry: *An Introduction* TB/548
GOTTLOB FREGE: The Foundations of Arithmetic: *A Logico-Mathematical Enquiry* TB/534
S. KÖRNER: The Philosophy of Mathematics: *An Introduction* TB/547
D. E. LITTLEWOOD: Skeleton Key of Mathematics: *A Simple Account of Complex Algebraic Problems* TB/525
GEORGE E. OWEN: Fundamentals of Scientific Mathematics TB/569
WILLARD VAN ORMAN QUINE: Mathematical Logic TB/558
O. G. SUTTON: Mathematics in Action. ° *Foreword by James R. Newman. Illus.* TB/518
FREDERICK WAISMANN: Introduction to Mathematical Thinking. *Foreword by Karl Menger* TB/511

Philosophy of Science

R. B. BRAITHWAITE: Scientific Explanation TB/515
J. BRONOWSKI: Science and Human Values. *Revised and Enlarged Edition* TB/505
ALBERT EINSTEIN et al.: Albert Einstein: Philosopher-Scientist. *Edited by Paul A. Schilpp* Vol. I TB/502; Vol. II TB/503
WERNER HEISENBERG: Physics and Philosophy: *The Revolution in Modern Science* TB/549
JOHN MAYNARD KEYNES: A Treatise on Probability. ° *Introduction by N. R. Hanson* TB/557
KARL R. POPPER: The Logic of Scientific Discovery TB/576
STEPHEN TOULMIN: Foresight and Understanding: *An Enquiry into the Aims of Science. Foreword by Jacques Barzun* TB/564
STEPHEN TOULMIN: The Philosophy of Science: *An Introduction* TB/513
G. J. WHITROW: The Natural Philosophy of Time ° TB/563

Physics and Cosmology

STEPHEN TOULMIN & JUNE GOODFIELD: The Fabric of the Heavens: *The Development of Astronomy and Dynamics. Illus.* TB/579
DAVID BOHM: Causality and Chance in Modern Physics. *Foreword by Louis de Broglie* TB/536
P. W. BRIDGMAN: The Nature of Thermodynamics TB/537
P. W. BRIDGMAN: A Sophisticate's Primer of Relativity TB/575
A. C. CROMBIE, Ed.: Turning Point in Physics TB/535
C. V. DURELL: Readable Relativity. *Foreword by Freeman J. Dyson* TB/530
ARTHUR EDDINGTON: Space, Time and Gravitation: *An Outline of the General Relativity Theory* TB/510
GEORGE GAMOW: Biography of Physics Σ TB/567
MAX JAMMER: Concepts of Force: *A Study in the Foundation of Dynamics* TB/550
MAX JAMMER: Concepts of Mass *in Classical and Modern Physics* TB/571
MAX JAMMER: Concepts of Space: *The History of Theories of Space in Physics. Foreword by Albert Einstein* TB/533
EDMUND WHITTAKER: History of the Theories of Aether and Electricity
Volume I: *The Classical Theories* TB/531
Volume II: *The Modern Theories* TB/532
G. J. WHITROW: The Structure and Evolution of the Universe: *An Introduction to Cosmology. Illus.* TB/504